Workbook

DIMENSIONS MATH 7B

a Singapore Math® Program

 STAR PUBLISHING PTE LTD

 Singapore Math Inc®

 **STAR PUBLISHING PTE LTD**

Star Publishing Pte Ltd
115A Commonwealth Drive #05-12
Singapore 149596
Tel: (65) 64796800
Website: www.starpub.com.sg
Email: contactus@starpub.com.sg

in association with

 Singapore Math Inc®

Singapore Math Inc
Red Soils Business Park
404 S Beavercreek Road, Suite #225
Oregon City, OR 97045
Tel: (503) 557-8100 Ext 104
Website: www.SingaporeMath.com
Email: customerservice@singaporemath.com

Based on the original series entitled
Discovering Mathematics, approved by
Ministry of Education, Singapore.

First published 2013
Reprinted 2016
Reprinted 2018
Reprinted 2019
Dimensions Math has been adapted from
Discovering Mathematics, first published by
Star Publishing Pte Ltd in 2007.

ISBN 978-981-4431-75-0

Printed by KHL Printing Co Pte Ltd, Singapore

PREFACE

The **Dimensions Math Common Core Workbooks** are designed for middle school students. Developed in collaboration between Star Publishing Pte. Ltd. and Singapore Math Inc., these workbooks follow the Singapore Mathematics Framework and also cover the topics in the Common Core State Standards.

Each workbook is written as a supplement to the textbook, *Dimensions Math Common Core*, to give students more practice in applying the concepts learned. Students may refer to the summary of the important concepts in each chapter of the textbook for a quick review before attempting the questions in the workbook. After completing the exercises, students will not only polish their own analytical skills, but also develop a stronger foundation in mathematics.

The questions in each workbook chapter are categorized into 4 parts according to the level of difficulty and the thinking skills involved:

Basic Practice: simple questions that drill comprehension of concepts
Further Practice: harder questions that involve direct applications
Challenging Practice: questions that require synthesis ability
Enrichment: questions that demand higher order thinking

These questions encourage students to think analytically, reason logically, use appropriate connections between mathematical ideas, and apply problem-solving skills in daily life situations.

We hope that these comprehensive workbooks will give students the tools and the confidence to handle mathematical questions and apply mathematical concepts to real-life situations. By achieving this, students will find learning mathematic an interesting and exciting experience.

We wish to express our sincere thanks to all those who have provided valuable feedback and assistance in the production of these workbooks.

The Writing Team
Dimensions Math Common Core

CONTENTS

9 Number Patterns

1. Write down the next two terms of each sequence.
   (a) 4, 7, 10, 13, …
   (b) 7, 15, 23, 31, …
   (c) 13, 25, 37, 49, …
   (d) 25, 38, 51, 64, …
   (e) 27, 23, 19, 15, …
   (f) 37, 28, 19, 10, …
   (g) 23, 16, 9, 2, …
   (h) 56, 40, 24, 8, …

2. Write down the next two terms of each sequence.
   (a) 1, 3, 9, 27, …
   (b) 0.5, 2, 8, 32, …
   (c) 8, 12, 18, 27, …
   (d) 128, 64, 32, 16, …
   (e) 6, –12, 24, –48, …
   (f) –2, 8, –32, 128, …
   (g) 1,600, –800, 400, –200, …
   (h) –3,125, 625, –125, 25, …

3. Write down the next two terms of each sequence.
   (a) 5, 6, 8, 11, 15, …
   (b) 3, 5, 9, 15, 23, …
   (c) 6, 9, 14, 21, 30, …
   (d) 7, 6, 8, 7, 9, …
   (e) 1, 2, 6, 24, 120, …
   (f) $\dfrac{1}{2}, \dfrac{3}{4}, \dfrac{5}{6}, \dfrac{7}{8}, \ldots$
   (g) $\dfrac{2}{5}, \dfrac{5}{12}, \dfrac{8}{19}, \dfrac{11}{26}, \ldots$
   (h) $\dfrac{1}{2}, \dfrac{3}{5}, \dfrac{8}{13}, \dfrac{21}{34}, \ldots$

4. Find the first 3 terms of each sequence from the given general term T_n.
   (a) $T_n = 3n + 5$
   (b) $T_n = -4n + 9$
   (c) $T_n = -5n - 8$
   (d) $T_n = \dfrac{18 - n}{2}$
   (e) $T_n = (2n + 7)^2$
   (f) $T_n = (n + 9)(5n - 2)$
   (g) $T_n = 2n(n - 1)(2n - 1)$
   (h) $T_n = \dfrac{3n - 2}{2n + 1}$

5. Find the 8th term of each sequence from the given general term T_n.
   (a) $T_n = 7n + 3$
   (b) $T_n = 2(n - 12)$
   (c) $T_n = 5n(3 - 4n)$
   (d) $T_n = (3n + 4)(2n + 3)(n - 2)$
   (e) $T_n = \dfrac{40 + n}{3n}$
   (f) $T_n = \dfrac{21(2n - 4)}{n(n - 1)}$

6. The general term of a sequence is $T_n = 20n + 8$.
   (a) Write down the first 3 terms.
   (b) Find the greatest 2-digit number in the sequence.
   (c) Find the smallest 3-digit number in the sequence.

7. The general term of a sequence is $T_n = 32 - 7n$.
   (a) Write down the first 3 terms.
   (b) Find the 10th term.
   (c) (i) Find the smallest positive number in the sequence.
       (ii) Hence, write down the first negative number in the sequence.

8. The general term of a sequence is $T_n = (2n + 3)(4n - 9)$.
   (a) Find the 5th term and the 9th term.
   (b) Hence, find the sum of the 5th term and the 9th term.

9. The general term of a sequence is $T_n = 5n + 18$.
   (a) Find the value of p if the pth term is 63.
   (b) Find the value of q if the qth term is 88.

10. The general term of a sequence is $T_n = \dfrac{8n - 4}{3n + 1}$.
    (a) Find the value of p if the pth term is 2.
    (b) Find the value of q if the qth term is $2\dfrac{2}{5}$.

Further Practice

11. Find the 7th and 8th terms of each sequence.
    (a) 7, 11, 15, 19, ...   (b) 8, 15, 22, 29, ...
    (c) 29, 23, 17, 11, ...   (d) 50, 41, 32, 23, ...
    (e) 2, –8, 32, –128, ...   (f) 32, 48, 72, 108, ...
    (g) 729, 486, 324, 216, ...   (h) –384, 192, –96, 48, ...

12. A sequence is formed by $3 \times (1 + 2)$, $3 \times (2 + 2)$, $3 \times (3 + 2)$, $3 \times (4 + 2)$, ...
    (a) Write down the values of the first 4 terms of the sequence.
    (b) Find the 10th term of the sequence.
    (c) Is 41 a term in the sequence? Explain your answer.

13. A sequence is formed by $\dfrac{1^2 - 3}{2}$, $\dfrac{2^2 - 3}{2}$, $\dfrac{3^2 - 3}{2}$, $\dfrac{4^2 - 3}{2}$, ...
    (a) Write down the values of the first 4 terms of the sequence.
    (b) Find the 10th term of the sequence.
    (c) Show that 75.4 is not a term in the sequence.

14. Find the general term, T_n of each sequence.
  (a) 4, 7, 10, 13, ...
  (b) 5, 12, 19, 26, ...
  (c) −8, 1, 10, 19, ...
  (d) 7, 3, −1, −5, ...
  (e) 34, 23, 12, 1, ...
  (f) 45, 37, 29, 21, ...

15. A sequence is formed by $4 \times (3 - 2)^2, 4 \times (4 - 2)^2, 4 \times (5 - 2)^2, 4 \times (6 - 2)^2, ...$
  (a) Write down the general term, T_n.
  (b) Hence, find the 8th term.
  (c) Is every term in the sequence a perfect square? Explain your answer.

16. A sequence is formed by $2^2 - 1^2, 3^2 - 2^2, 4^2 - 3^2, 5^2 - 4^2, ...$
  (a) Write down the values of the first 4 terms of the sequence.
  (b) Hence, by recognizing the pattern, evaluate the following without using a calculator.
    (i) $17^2 - 16^2$,
    (ii) $29^2 - 28^2$,
    (iii) $62^2 - 61^2$.
  (c) Deduce and write down the general term, T_n of the sequence.

17. The first 4 terms of a sequence are 38, 32, 26, and 20.
  (a) Find its general term, T_n.
  (b) Hence, find the general term, T_n of a sequence if its first 4 terms are
    (i) 41, 35, 29, and 23,
    (ii) 34, 28, 22, and 16,
    (iii) 19, 16, 13, and 10.

18. The general term of a sequence is $T_n = 4n + 7$.
  (a) The sum of 2 consecutive terms in the sequence is 82. Find the 2 terms.
  (b) The sum of 3 consecutive terms in the sequence is 165. Find the 3 terms.

19. The diagram shows a sequence of equilateral triangles formed by toothpicks. Each toothpick is 6 cm long.

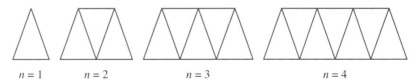

$n = 1$ $n = 2$ $n = 3$ $n = 4$

Let the number of toothpicks and the perimeter, in cm, of the nth pattern be T_n and P_n respectively.
  (a) Complete the following table.

n	1	2	3	4
T_n	3			
P_n	18			

  (b) (i) Find an expression for T_n.
    (ii) Hence, find T_7 and T_8.
  (c) (i) Find an expression for P_n.
    (ii) Hence, find P_7 and P_8.

20. The diagram shows a sequence of patterns formed by squares and dots.

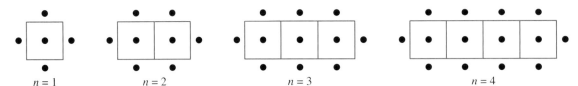

Let the number of squares and dots in the nth pattern be S_n and D_n respectively.
(a) Write down D_1, D_2, D_3, and D_4.
(b) Express D_n in terms of S_n.
(c) Hence, find
    (i) the number of dots if there are 15 squares,
    (ii) the number of squares if there are 62 dots.

Challenging Practice

21. A piece of writing paper is cut into 2 equal portions, A and B. Portion A is collected and portion B is cut into 2 equal portions, C and D. Portion C is collected and portion D is cut into 2 equal portions, E and F. The process goes on for as many times as possible.

The sum of the portions which are collected after each cut at the nth stage can be represented by the sequence $\dfrac{1}{2}, \dfrac{1}{2} + \dfrac{1}{4}, \dfrac{1}{2} + \dfrac{1}{4} + \dfrac{1}{8}, \dfrac{1}{2} + \dfrac{1}{4} + \dfrac{1}{8} + \dfrac{1}{16}, \dots$, i.e., $\dfrac{1}{2}, \dfrac{3}{4}, \dfrac{7}{8}, \dfrac{15}{16}, \dots$

(a) Find the next 2 terms.
(b) Deduce and write down the general term, T_n.
(c) Hence, estimate the value of $\dfrac{1}{2} + \dfrac{1}{4} + \dfrac{1}{8} + \dfrac{1}{16} + \dots$ if n is a large number.

22. The diagram shows a sequence of figures formed by small shaded and unshaded triangles.

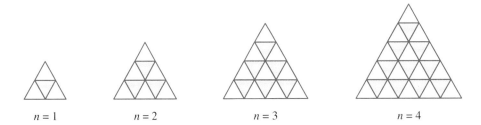

Let the number of small shaded and unshaded triangles in the nth figure be S_n and U_n respectively.
(a) Draw the 5th figure.
(b) Write down
    (i) S_1, S_2, S_3, and S_4,
    (ii) U_1, U_2, U_3, and U_4,
    (iii) $S_1 + U_1$, $S_2 + U_2$, $S_3 + U_3$, and $S_4 + U_4$.
(c) **(i)** Hence, deduce and write down an expression for $S_n + U_n$ in terms of n.
    (ii) Find the total number of small triangles in the 15th figure.

23. The diagram shows a sequence of figures formed by small circles and hexagons.

  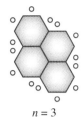 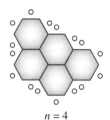

$n = 1$ $n = 2$ $n = 3$ $n = 4$

Let the number of hexagons and circles in the nth pattern be H_n and C_n respectively.

(a) Draw the 5th figure.

(b) Complete the following table.

n	1	2	3	4
H_n	2			
C_n	10			

(c) Find an expression for
    (i) H_n,
    (ii) C_n.

(d) Find
    (i) the number of circles if there are 10 hexagons,
    (ii) the number of hexagons if there are 50 circles.

(e) Can a figure have $(2p + 1)$ circles, where p is a positive integer? Explain your answer.

24. The diagram shows a sequence of rectangular figures formed by dots. The distance between the centers of any 2 adjacent dots is 2 cm.

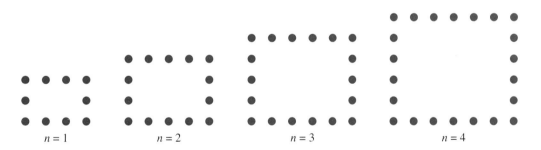

$n = 1$ $n = 2$ $n = 3$ $n = 4$

Let the number of dots and the area of the nth rectangular figure be D_n and A_n cm^2 respectively.

(a) Draw the 5th figure.

(b) Write down
    (i) D_1, D_2, D_3, and D_4,
    (ii) A_1, A_2, A_3, and A_4.

(c) **(i)** Find an expression for D_n.
    (ii) Hence, find the number of dots in the 12th figure.

(d) **(i)** Express A_n as a product of 2 factors in terms of n.
    (ii) Hence, find the area of the 12th figure.

(e) The number of dots in the pth figure is 62. Find
    (i) the value of p,
    (ii) the area of the corresponding figure.

5

25. A square of 4 numbers is selected from the following array of 30 consecutive numbers. Two such squares are shown below.

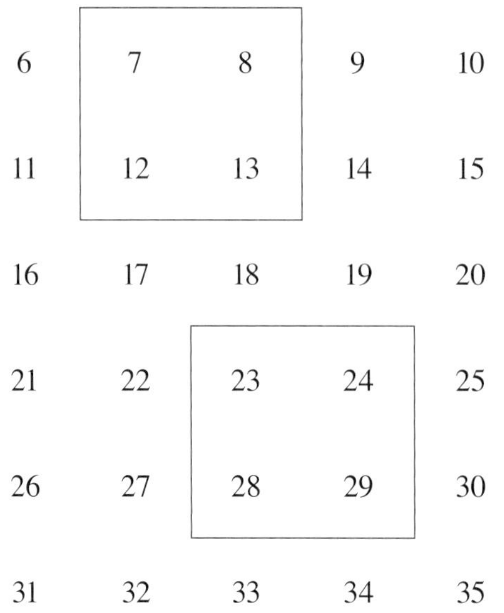

6	7	8	9	10
11	12	13	14	15
16	17	18	19	20
21	22	23	24	25
26	27	28	29	30
31	32	33	34	35

(a) If the number at the top left-hand corner of a selected square is x, find, in terms of x,
   (i) the other 3 numbers,
   (ii) the sum of the 4 numbers.
(b) Show that the sum of the 4 numbers in any selected square is a multiple of 4.
(c) The sum of the 4 numbers in a selected square is 88. Use your answer in **(a)(ii)** to find the value of the greatest number in the square.

26. (a) Find the value of each of the following.

(i) $\dfrac{1}{1 \times 3}$

(ii) $\dfrac{1}{1 \times 3} + \dfrac{1}{3 \times 5}$

(iii) $\dfrac{1}{1 \times 3} + \dfrac{1}{3 \times 5} + \dfrac{1}{5 \times 7}$

(iv) $\dfrac{1}{1 \times 3} + \dfrac{1}{3 \times 5} + \dfrac{1}{5 \times 7} + \dfrac{1}{7 \times 9}$

(b) Hence, suggest the value of each of the following sums.

(i) $\dfrac{1}{1 \times 3} + \dfrac{1}{3 \times 5} + \dfrac{1}{5 \times 7} + \ldots + \dfrac{1}{17 \times 19}$

(ii) $\dfrac{1}{1 \times 3} + \dfrac{1}{3 \times 5} + \dfrac{1}{5 \times 7} + \ldots + \dfrac{1}{(2n - 1)(2n + 1)}$

27. Consider the sequence $8x + y$, $7x + 3y$, $6x + 5y$, $5x + 7y$, ...

(a) Write down the 5th term and the 6th term of the sequence.

(b) Suggest the formula for the nth term of the sequence.

(c) If the nth term of the sequence is $-3x + 23y$, find the value of n.

28.

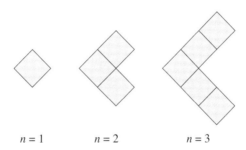

$n = 1$ $n = 2$ $n = 3$

Square tiles of length 5 cm are used to form patterns as shown above.

(a) Draw the patterns for $n = 4$ and $n = 5$.

(b) Complete the following table where M_n is the number of tiles and P_n cm is the perimeter of the nth pattern.

n	1	2	3	4	5
M_n					
P_n					

(c) Find the general term of M_n.

(d) Find the general term of P_n.

29. In the diagram below, the number of dots in the nth pattern is called the nth pentagonal number, that is, the first 4 pentagonal numbers are 1, 5, 12, and 22.

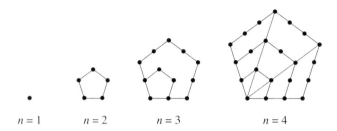

$n = 1$ $n = 2$ $n = 3$ $n = 4$

(a) Draw the patterns for $n = 5$ and $n = 6$.

(b) Write down the 5th and 6th pentagonal numbers.

(c) Suggest the general term a_n of the nth pentagonal number.

10 Coordinates And Linear Graphs

Basic Practice

1. (a) Write down the coordinates of the points
        A to J in the given diagram.
    (b) Write down the points that have positive
        x-coordinates.
    (c) Write down the points that have negative
        y-coordinates.

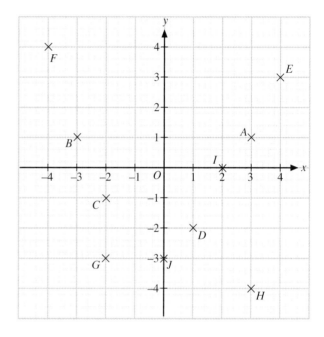

2. (a) Plot each of the following points in the
        given diagram.
        (i)   A(2, 3)
        (ii)   B(−4, 2)
        (iii)   C(−3, 0)
        (iv)   D(−2, −4)
        (v)   E(4, −2)
        (vi)   F(0, 4)
        (vii)   G(3.2, 2)
        (viii) H(−0.8, −2)
        (ix)   I(2.6, −3.4)
        (x)   J(−3.4, 3.6)
    (b) Which points are in the second quadrant?
    (c) Which points are in the third quadrant?

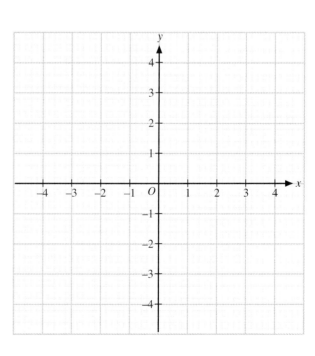

3. (a) Plot the points $P(-5, -4)$, $Q(1, -4)$, and $R(1, 3)$ on a coordinate plane.
   (b) (i) Join PQ, QR, and RP.
       (ii) Classify $\triangle PQR$ by its angles.
   (c) Find the area of $\triangle PQR$.

4. (a) Copy and complete the following table.

x	-2	-1	0	1	2
$y = 2x + 1$					

   (b) Draw the graph of $y = 2x + 1$ from $x = -2$ to $x = 2$.
   (c) Find the point at which the graph cuts the x-axis.
   (d) A point A lies on the graph. If its x-coordinate is $\frac{1}{2}$, find its y-coordinate.
   (e) A point B lies on the graph. If its y-coordinate is 4, find its x-coordinate.

5. (a) Copy and complete the following table.

x	-2	0	2	4	6
$y = -x + 5$					

   (b) Draw the graph of $y = -x + 5$ from $x = -2$ to $x = 6$.
   (c) Does the point $A(3, 3)$ lie on the graph?
   (d) (i) Draw the line $x = -1$ on the same coordinate plane in (b).
       (ii) Find the point at which the graph of $y = -x + 5$ and the line $x = -1$ meet.

6. (a) Draw the graph of $y = \frac{2}{3}x - 4$ from $x = -3$ to $x = 9$.
   (b) Find the point at which the graph cuts the x-axis.
   (c) Does the point $B\left(7\frac{1}{2}, 1\right)$ lie on the graph?

7. (a) Draw the graph of $y = \frac{6 - x}{2}$ from $x = -2$ to $x = 8$.
   (b) Find the point at which the graph cuts
       (i) the x-axis,
       (ii) the y-axis.
   (c) Locate and write down the point on the graph in which the x-coordinate of the point is equal to its y-coordinate.

8. (a) Draw the following lines on the same diagram.
       (i) $x = -2$
       (ii) $x = 4$
       (iii) $y = -1$
       (iv) $y = 5$
   (b) (i) Write down the coordinates of all the vertices of the quadrilateral formed by the intersection of the lines in (a).
       (ii) Classify this quadrilateral by its sides.

9. Find the slopes of the lines L_1, L_2, L_3, L_4, and L_5 in the following diagram.

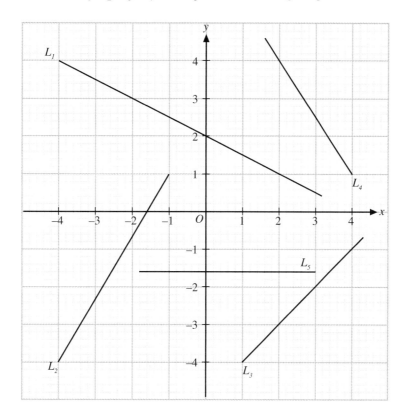

10. Find the slopes of the lines L_1, L_2, L_3, and L_4 in the following diagram.

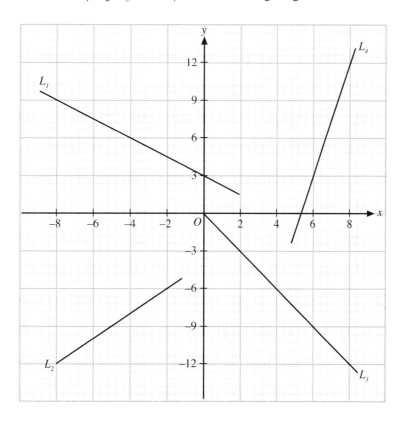

11. (a) Plot the points $A(-3, 3)$, $B(1, 3)$, $C(4, 0)$, and $D(4, -4)$ on a coordinate plane.
   (b) What type of quadrilateral is $ABCD$?
   (c) (i) Draw the perpendicular bisectors of AB and CD.
      (ii) Write down the coordinates of the point where the two perpendicular bisectors meet.

12. (a) Plot the points $P(4, 6)$, $Q(2, 1)$, and $R(-3, -1)$ on a coordinate plane.
   (b) Classify $\triangle PQR$ by the lengths of its sides.
   (c) Find the coordinates of the point S such that the y-axis is the perpendicular bisector of the line segment RS.
   (d) Find the coordinates of the point T such that the x-axis is the perpendicular bisector of the line segment QT.

13. (a) Plot the points $D(-4, -1)$, $E(1, -3)$, and $F(4, -1)$ on a coordinate plane.
   (b) (i) State the quadrant in which the point D lies.
      (ii) State the quadrant in which the point E lies.
   (c) Find the coordinates of the point G such that $DEFG$ is a parallelogram.
   (d) Find the coordinates of the point H such that $DEFH$ is a kite.

14. (a) Draw the graph of $y = -2x + 5$ from $x = -2$ to $x = 6$.
   (b) A is a point on the graph.
      (i) Find the coordinates of A if its x-coordinate is $-1\frac{1}{2}$.
      (ii) State the quadrant in which A lies.
   (c) B is a point on the graph.
      (i) Find the coordinates of B if its y-coordinate is -4.
      (ii) State the quadrant in which B lies.

15. (a) Draw the graph of $y = 2(2x - 3)$ from $x = -4$ to $x = 4$.
   (b) (i) The points $A\left(1\frac{1}{2}, p\right)$ and $B(q, 0)$ lie on the graph. Find the values of p and q graphically.
      (ii) Hence, write down a relationship between the points A and B.
   (c) Locate and write down a point on the graph in which the y-coordinate of the point is twice its x-coordinate.

16. (a) Draw the following lines on the same diagram.
      (i) $x = -4$
      (ii) $x = 5$
      (iii) $y = -3$
      (iv) $y = 3$
   (b) (i) Sub-divide the rectangle formed by the lines in **(a)** into 9 equal portions by drawing 2 horizontal lines and 2 vertical lines on the same diagram.
      (ii) Write down the equation of each line drawn in **(b)(i)**.
   (c) The intersection of the horizontal and vertical lines drawn in **(b)(i)** form a small rectangle $ABCD$.
      (i) Write down the coordinates of the vertices of rectangle $ABCD$.
      (ii) Find the ratio of the perimeters of rectangle $ABCD$ and the rectangle formed by the lines in **(a)**.

17. Find the value of p in each of the following.
  (a) $(3, 2p)$ lies on the graph of $y = 5x + 9$.
  (b) $(6p, -7)$ lies on the graph of $y = 2x - 11$.
  (c) (p, p) lies on the graph of $y = -2(x - 6)$.

18. (a) Plot the points $A(-4, -1)$, $B(-1, -2)$, and $C(2, -1)$ on a coordinate plane.
  (b) Find and plot the coordinates of the point D such that $ABCD$ is a rhombus.
  (c) Find the slopes of the sides of $ABCD$.
  (d) Suggest a relationship between the slopes of the opposite sides of a rhombus.

19. (a) The slopes of the lines AB and AC are 0 and undefined respectively. What can be deduced about AB and AC?
  (b) Plot the points $B(-3, -2)$ and $C(1, 6)$ on a coordinate plane. Find
    (i) the slope of BC,   **(ii)** the coordinates of A.
  (c) State the coordinates of the midpoint M of B and C.
  (d) Find the slope of the line segment AM.

20. (a) Plot the points $A(-5, -4)$, $B(-3, 0)$, and $C(2, 10)$ on a coordinate plane.
  (b) Find the slope of
    (i) the line segment AB,   **(ii)** the line segment BC.
  (c) What can be deduced about the points A, B, and C?

Challenging Practice

21. The points A, B, C, and D are located on the given diagram. Given that the x- and y-coordinates of the points A, B, C, and D are positive integers, find the possible coordinates of
  (a) the point A such that the x-coordinate of A is 3 times its y-coordinate,
  (b) the point B such that the x-coordinate of B is 4 more than its y-coordinate,
  (c) the point C such that both the x- and y-coordinates of C are prime numbers,
  (d) the point D such that the x-coordinate of D is a multiple of 3 and its y-coordinate is a perfect cube.

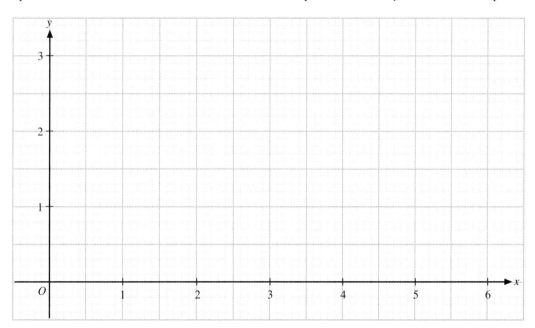

22. (a) (i) Plot the points $A(-5, 3)$ and $B(5, -2)$ on a coordinate plane.

   (ii) Find the slope of the line segment AB.

   (b) A point C lies on AB. Find the coordinates of C if its y-coordinate is 2.

   (c) A point D lies on AB. Find the coordinates of D if it also lies on the x-axis.

   (d) Show that the point A lies on the graph of $y = -\dfrac{1}{5}x + 2$.

   (e) Hence, can it be concluded that the points B, C, and D also lie on the graph of $y = -\dfrac{1}{5}x + 2$? Explain your answer.

23. The taxi fare $\$y$ for a journey during off-peak hours is given by $y = \dfrac{4}{5}x + \dfrac{5}{2}$ where x is the distance traveled in miles.

   (a) Draw the graph of $y = \dfrac{4}{5}x + \dfrac{5}{2}$ for $0 \leqslant x \leqslant 10$.

   (b) Find the slope of the graph and interpret its physical meaning.

   (c) What is the physical meaning of $\dfrac{5}{2}$ in the equation $y = \dfrac{4}{5}x + \dfrac{5}{2}$?

   (d) Use your graph to estimate
   (i) the taxi fare if the distance traveled is 7.5 miles,
   (ii) the distance traveled if the taxi fare is $\$4.50$.

24. On average, the mass y kg of a young goat x months after it arrived at the farm is given by $y = 2x + 30$ for $0 \leqslant x \leqslant 5$.

   (a) Draw the graph of $y = 2x + 30$ for $0 \leqslant x \leqslant 5$.

   (b) Find the slope of the graph and interpret its physical meaning.

   (c) Find the mass of the goat when it arrived at the farm.

   (d) Use your graph to estimate
   (i) the increase in the goat's mass $1\dfrac{1}{2}$ months after it arrived at the farm,
   (ii) the number of months after which the goat gained 5 kg.

25. The distance y_1 meters of a boy at time t seconds from a fixed point O is given by $y_1 = t + 20$ for $0 \leqslant t \leqslant 50$. The distance y_2 meters of the boy's father at time t seconds from the same fixed point O is given by $y_2 = 2t$ for $0 \leqslant t \leqslant 50$.

   (a) Draw the graphs of $y_1 = t + 20$ and $y_2 = 2t$ for $0 \leqslant t \leqslant 50$ on the same diagram.

   (b) Is the boy or his father moving faster? Explain your answer.

   (c) Suppose that the boy and his father are moving in the same direction. Use your graphs to find the distance between them after 15 seconds.

   (d) After p seconds, both of them are q meters from O. Use your graphs to find the values of p and q.

26. In the diagram, *ABCD* is a square, the vertices *A* and *D* are (5, 0) and (0, 3) respectively.
    (a) Find the coordinates of the vertices *B* and *C*.
    (b) Calculate the area of *ABCD*.

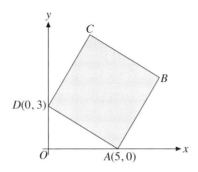

27. Aaron uses the coordinate plane below to compile secret codes. The code for '*BYE*' is '(2, 5), (1, 1), (5, 5)'.
    (a) Find the code for '*DEAR*'.
    (b) If the code is '(4, 3), (3, 4), (6, 4), (6, 4), (3, 3), (5, 2)', write down the word.
    (c) Find the slope of the line joining *T* and *Q*.

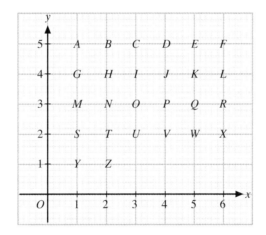

28. (a) Plot the points (−4, 3), (−2, 2), (0, 1), and (2, 0) in the diagram provided.
    (b) Describe the relationship between the points.
    (c) Write down an equation to represent the relationship in (b).

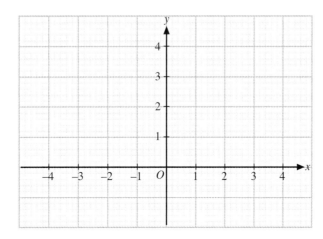

29. A class of students prepared some screen printing T-shirts and sold them for fund raising. The profit y for selling x T-shirts was given by $y = 4x - 100$, for $0 \leqslant x \leqslant 80$.

   (a) Complete the following table.

x	0	20	40	60	80
y					

   (b) Using a scale of 1 cm representing 10 units on the x-axis and 1 cm representing 50 units on the y-axis, draw the graph of $y = 4x - 100$.
   (c) When no T-shirts were sold, what was the profit?
   (d) How many T-shirts had to be sold in order to break even, i.e., there was no profit or loss?
   (e) How many T-shirts must be sold to earn a profit of $100?
   (f) Find the slope of the graph and interpret its meaning.

11 Inequalities

Basic Practice

1. In each of the following, determine whether the specified value of x is a solution of the given inequality.
   (a) $x > 10$; $x = 19$
   (b) $x < 5$; $x = 5$
   (c) $x < -12$; $x = -2$
   (d) $x > -23$; $x = -6$
   (e) $x \geqslant 34$; $x = 34$
   (f) $4x \leqslant 20$; $x = -1$
   (g) $5x > 7$; $x = 1.2$
   (h) $3x \geqslant -2$; $x = -\dfrac{1}{2}$
   (i) $\dfrac{x}{2} \geqslant -5$; $x = -11$
   (j) $\dfrac{3}{5}x < 9$; $x = -\dfrac{3}{5}$

2. Solve the following inequalities.
   (a) $2x > 12$
   (b) $4x > 32$
   (c) $3x < -18$
   (d) $5x < 22.5$
   (e) $6x \geqslant 27$
   (f) $8x \geqslant -30$
   (g) $16x \leqslant 36$
   (h) $24x \leqslant -64$

3. (a) List all the positive even integers that are smaller than or equal to 20.
   (b) Find all possible values of x in each of the following inequalities if x is a positive even integer that is smaller than or equal to 20.
   (i) $x < 10$
   (ii) $x > 12$
   (iii) $x \leqslant 9$
   (iv) $x \geqslant 14$
   (v) $2x < 8$
   (vi) $3x > 51$
   (vii) $5x \leqslant 21$
   (viii) $4x \geqslant 71$

4. (a) List all the prime numbers that are smaller than or equal to 30.
   (b) Find all possible values of x in each of the following inequalities if x is a prime number that is smaller than 30.
   (i) $x < 15$
   (ii) $x > 23$
   (iii) $x \leqslant 17$
   (iv) $x \geqslant 22$
   (v) $4x < 28$
   (vi) $5x > 45$
   (vii) $2x \leqslant 7$
   (viii) $3x \geqslant 43$

5. **(a)** List all the odd numbers that are greater than –7 but smaller than 7.
   (b) Find all possible values of x in each of the following inequalities if x is an odd number that is greater than –7 but smaller than 7.

(i) $\quad x < -1$	**(ii)** $\quad x > 3$
(iii) $\quad x \leqslant -2$	**(iv)** $\quad x \geqslant 4$
(v) $\quad 7x < -14$	**(vi)** $\quad 6x > -18$
(vii) $\quad 4x \leqslant -17$	**(viii)** $\quad 12x \geqslant 45$

6. Given that $x > 9$, find the smallest possible value of x if x is
   (a) an integer,
   (b) an odd number,
   (c) a prime number,
   (d) a perfect square,
   (e) a perfect cube.

7. Fill in each box with an inequality sign to make each of the following statements correct.

   (a) If $x > y$, then $x + 4 \boxed{} y + 4.$

   (b) If $m \leqslant n$, then $3m \boxed{} 3n.$

   (c) If $c < d$, then $-5c \boxed{} -5d.$

   (d) If $v \geqslant w$, then $\dfrac{v}{-2} \boxed{} \dfrac{w}{-2}.$

   (e) If $a > b$, then $2a - 7 \boxed{} 2b - 7.$

   (f) If $r \leqslant s$, then $-8r + 9 \boxed{} -8s + 9.$

   (g) If $p = q + 6$, then $p \boxed{} q.$

   (h) If $g = h - 10$, then $g \boxed{} h.$

8. Solve each of the following inequalities and represent the solution on a number line.

(a) $\ x + 5 > 12$	**(b)** $\ 2x - 9 < 21$
(c) $\ 3x + 10 \geqslant 16$	**(d)** $\ 8 - x < 15$
(e) $\ 17 - 3x \geqslant 26$	**(f)** $\ 4x + 13 < 33 - x$
(g) $\ 45 - 8x \leqslant 5x - 7$	**(h)** $\ \dfrac{x}{2} + 7 > 5$

9. **(a)** Find the smallest integer value of x that satisfies each of the following inequalities.
   (i) $\quad 2x - 7 > 15$
   (ii) $\quad 5x + 9 > x$
   (iii) $6x - 13 \geqslant 4x - 15$
   (iv) $1 - 7x \leqslant 8 - 2x$
   (b) Find the greatest integer value of x that satisfies each of the following inequalities.
   (i) $\quad 3x + 8 < 20$
   (ii) $\quad 10x - 25 \leqslant 6x$
   (iii) $x + 19 < 2 - x$
   (iv) $4(9 - x) \geqslant 3(2 + x)$

10. The cost of a carton of milk is $2.
    (a) Find the total cost of x cartons of milk.
    (b) Find the possible numbers of cartons of milk Felicia can buy with $11.

11. The volume of an empty tank is x cm^3. Water is scooped and poured into the tank. Suppose that each scoop contains 120 cm^3 of water.
   (a) Express, in terms of x, the number of scoops that are needed to fill the tank completely with water.
   (b) Find the possible volume of the tank if the total number of scoops required is more than 15.

12. Joyce jogs for 30 minutes at an average speed of x km/hr.
   (a) Find, in terms of x, the distance Joyce covers in km.
   (b) Find, in km/hr, the possible average speed of Joyce if she covers more than 3.2 km.

13. The cost of an apple is 65 cents.
   (a) Find the cost of x apples.
   (b) **(i)** Find the maximum number of apples Mrs. White can buy with $5.50.
       (ii) If she buys the greatest possible number of apples, how much change will she receive?

(**Further Practice**)

14. Solve the following inequalities.
   (a) $\frac{1}{5}x > 3$
   (b) $\frac{1}{8}x < -\frac{5}{2}$
   (c) $\frac{2}{3}x \geqslant -8$
   (d) $\frac{4}{25}x \leqslant \frac{12}{5}$
   (e) $\frac{3}{5}x > -9$
   (f) $\frac{7}{33}x < -1\frac{3}{11}$
   (g) $1\frac{1}{6}x \geqslant \frac{21}{2}$
   (h) $2\frac{1}{2}x \leqslant 3\frac{3}{4}$

15. Solve the following inequalities.
   (a) $3x + 2x > 35$
   (b) $7x - 3x < -24$
   (c) $-2x + 8x \geqslant 9$
   (d) $\frac{1}{2}x + 4x \leqslant -18$
   (e) $\frac{1}{3}x - \frac{1}{4}x > \frac{3}{2}$
   (f) $\frac{1}{2}x + \frac{2}{3}x < -\frac{14}{3}$
   (g) $\frac{4}{5}x - \frac{3}{7}x \geqslant 26$
   (h) $\frac{5}{6}x - \frac{3}{4}x \leqslant -\frac{2}{3}$

16. In each of the following, find the smallest integer x that satisfies the inequality.
   (a) $2x > 18$
   (b) $5x > -47$
   (c) $\frac{2}{7}x > 5$
   (d) $\frac{3}{5}x > -3.6$
   (e) $3x \geqslant 24$
   (f) $7x \geqslant -45$
   (g) $\frac{3}{10}x \geqslant \frac{9}{2}$
   (h) $\frac{5}{12}x \geqslant -4$

17. In each of the following, find the greatest integer x that satisfies the inequality.

(a) $4x < 28$

(b) $6x < -50$

(c) $\dfrac{4}{9}x < 7$

(d) $\dfrac{3}{11}x < -\dfrac{5}{2}$

(e) $14x \leqslant 42$

(f) $4x \leqslant -33$

(g) $\dfrac{4}{3}x \leqslant \dfrac{16}{15}$

(h) $\dfrac{9}{16}x \leqslant -2\dfrac{17}{32}$

18. (a) Solve $3x - \dfrac{7}{4}x > 50$.

(b) Hence, find the smallest possible value of x if
    (i) x is an even number,
    (ii) x is a prime number,
    (iii) x is divisible by 12.

19. (a) Solve $\dfrac{2}{3}x - \dfrac{1}{5}x < 7$.

(b) Hence, list all possible values of x if
    (i) x is a positive multiple of 3,
    (ii) x is a positive factor of 60.

20. Solve each of the following inequalities and represent the solution on a number line.

(a) $\dfrac{3x - 4}{5} > \dfrac{2x + 7}{6}$

(b) $\dfrac{2(x + 5)}{3} \leqslant \dfrac{4(x - 6)}{5}$

(c) $\dfrac{5x - 9}{2} + 1 \leqslant \dfrac{4x + 1}{3}$

(d) $3 - \dfrac{x + 4}{4} < \dfrac{7x - 5}{3}$

(e) $\dfrac{3x + 1}{5} - \dfrac{2 - 3x}{3} \geqslant \dfrac{4x - 7}{6}$

(f) $\dfrac{10 + x}{7} < 4 - \dfrac{8x - 9}{2}$

(g) $\dfrac{x + 4}{2} + \dfrac{2x - 5}{5} > x - \dfrac{3x - 8}{4}$

(h) $\dfrac{x - 4}{5} - \dfrac{9 + 4x}{3} \geqslant \dfrac{x}{8} - \dfrac{5 - 3x}{3}$

21. Consider the sequence 12, 24, 36, 48, ...
Find
(a) the general term, T_n of the sequence,
(b) the smallest term in the sequence that is more than 100,
(c) the greatest term in the sequence that is less than or equal to 200.

22. The length and width of a rectangle are $3x$ cm and 5 cm respectively.
(a) Express, in terms of x, the area of the rectangle.
(b) (i)   Form an inequality in terms of x if the area of the rectangle is greater than or equal to 70 cm^2.
    (ii) Solve the inequality.
(c) Hence, find the minimum area of the rectangle if x is an integer.

23. All or a portion of a wire of length 84 cm is shaped into a square of side $5x$ cm.
    (a) Form an inequality in terms of x and solve it.
    (b) Hence, find the maximum perimeter of the square if x is an integer.

24. The monthly salary of Mr. Moore is \$3,000 before it is increased by \$$x$.
    (a) Express, in terms of x, the percentage increase in his salary.
    (b) Suppose that the percentage increase is less than 5%.
        (i) Form an inequality in terms of x and solve it.
        (ii) Hence, find the new salary of Mr. Moore if the increase in his salary is maximized and x is an integer.

25. To pass a culinary course with distinction, a candidate must score at least 75 points in the culinary examination. The examination consists of a practical component and a theory component and the maximum scores of the 2 components are 60 points and 40 points respectively.
    (a) Mrs. Baker scores 51 points in the practical component. What should she score in the theory component to obtain a distinction?
    (b) Susan scores 30 points in the theory component. What should she score in the practical component to obtain a distinction?

26. Deborah buys 10 apples and x oranges from a supermarket. Suppose that the costs of an apple and an orange are \$0.60 and \$0.55 respectively.
    (a) Form an inequality in x if Deborah can spend at most \$13 on the fruits.
    (b) Solve the inequality in **(a)**.
    (c) Hence, find the maximum number of oranges Deborah can buy.
    (d) If Deborah buys the greatest possible number of oranges, how much change will she receive?

27. An object moves at an average speed of $(x + 1)$ m/s for 20 seconds. It then moves at an average speed of $(2x - 5)$ m/s for the next 30 seconds.
    (a) Form an inequality in x if the average speed of the object during the 50 seconds is less than 4 m/s.
    (b) Solve the inequality in **(a)**.

28. In the figure, $\triangle ABC$ is an isosceles triangle with $AB = AC$. The lengths of AB, AC, and BC are $(2x + 7)$ cm, $\dfrac{y + 8}{2}$ cm, and 10 cm respectively.

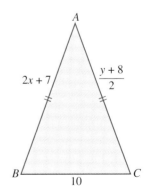

    (a) If $y = 38$, find
        (i) the value of x,
        (ii) the perimeter of $\triangle ABC$.
    (b) Suppose that the perimeter of $\triangle ABC$ is not more than 60 cm.
        (i) Form an inequality in x and solve it.
        (ii) Form an inequality in y and solve it.

29. (a) Solve the following inequalities.

    (i) $\dfrac{7}{4}x - \dfrac{5}{8}x > 27$ **(ii)** $\dfrac{4}{9}y + \dfrac{1}{6}y < 22$

(b) If x and y are integers, find

    (i) the smallest value of x,   **(ii)** the greatest value of y,

    (iii) the smallest value of $2x - y$.   **(iv)** the greatest value of $\dfrac{y}{x}$.

(c) Find the greatest value of $y - x$ if both x and y are multiples of 4.

30. Sarah is asked to buy cherry pies and apple pies in the ratio 2 : 3 for a social gathering. Suppose that each cherry pie costs 80 cents and each apple pie costs 90 cents.

(a) Find the total cost of $2x$ cherry pies and $3x$ apple pies.

(b) Sarah has \$18 to spend on the cherry pies and apple pies. Form an inequality in terms of x and solve it.

(c) Hence, find the maximum number of cherry pies and apple pies Sarah can buy.

(d) If she buys the greatest possible number of cherry pies and apple pies, how much change will she receive?

31. (a) Draw the graph of $y = 2x + 1$ for the values of x from -2 to 4.

(b) The points $(2, p)$ and $(q, 7)$ lie above the graph of $y = 2x + 1$. Find the possible values of

    (i) p,

    (ii) q.

(c) **(i)** Find the coordinates of the point that satisfies both **(b)(i)** and **(b)(ii)**.

    (ii) In which quadrant does this point lie?

32. Zackery has $(2x + 5)$ one-dollar bills, $(x - 8)$ five-dollar bills, $(2x + 3)$ ten-dollar bills, and x twenty-dollar bills.

(a) How much money does Zackery have in terms of x?

(b) If the total amount of money Zackery has is more than \$205, form an inequality in terms of x and solve it.

(c) Hence, find

    (i) the possible values of x,

    (ii) the smallest value of x,

    (iii) the minimum amount of money Zackery has.

33. Mr. Smith drives at an average speed of $2x$ km/hr for 15 minutes and then at an average speed of $4x$ km/hr for the next 20 minutes.

(a) Find the total distance traveled in km.

(b) Find the average speed for the whole journey in km/h.

(c) For the whole journey, Mr. Smith estimates he covered more than 50 km at an average speed of less than 80 km/hr. Is his estimation reasonable? Explain your answer.

34. The table below shows the taxi fare structures of 2 taxi operators, *Star Transport* and *Regent Pte. Ltd.* during the off-peak hours.

	Star Transport	Regent Pte. Ltd.
Flag down fee	$2.00	$3.00
Charge for 1st 500 m	Free	–
Charge for 1st 200 m	–	Free
Charge for every 100 m thereafter	$0.15	$0.10

(a) Calculate the fare charged by each operator for a journey of x km.

(b) Find the range of distances for which it is more affordable to take a taxi from *Star Transport*.

35. Hogan is given a budget of $1,200 to source desks and chairs for his company. Suppose he has to purchase more than 5 desks and more than 15 chairs and the costs of a desk and a chair are $90 and $24 respectively.

(a) Find the number of desks and number of chairs that can be purchased if the total number of items purchased is the least.

(b) Find the number of desks and number of chairs that can be purchased if the total number of items purchased is the greatest.

36. A wooden pencil costs 30 cents and a pen costs 55 cents. Sharon is given $9.50 and is told to spend the money as much as possible on at least one pencil and at least one pen. However, for every pen that she buys, she must buy at least 3 pencils.

(a) (i) Find the number of pencils and the number of pens that Sharon can buy if she has to buy the greatest possible number of items.

(ii) Hence, calculate the corresponding amount that Sharon must pay.

(b) (i) Find the number of pencils and the number of pens that Sharon can buy if she has to buy the least possible number of items.

(ii) Hence, calculate the corresponding amount that Sharon must pay.

(**Enrichment**)

37. (a) The price of a bowl is 250% of the price of a spoon. The price of a set of one bowl and one spoon is not greater than $6.30. Find the range of the price of the spoon.

(b) The mass of a bowl is 120 g. The maximum loading of a carry bag is 3 kg. Find the maximum number of bowls that can be carried by the bag.

38. (a) A condominium building has 30 levels and each level has 6 units. Each unit has either 2 bedrooms or 3 bedrooms. Estimate the range of the total number of bedrooms in the building.

(b) The price per m^2 of a unit in the building ranges from $9,000 to $12,000. Mr. Miller's budget for purchasing a unit is $960,000. Find the range of the area of a unit that can meet his budget.

39. The marked price of a jacket is $150. A shopkeeper increases the price by 20% and then sells it at a discount.
   (a) Find the selling price of the jacket when the discount is
      (i) 20%,
      (ii) 10%.
   (b) Find the range of discount percentage so that the selling price is greater than the original marked price.

40. Along a road, Tim's average speeds of walking and cycling are 4 km/hr and 20 km/hr respectively. He walks in one direction, and then cycles back to the starting point. His total time taken is less than 3 hours. Find
   (a) the possible distance traveled in one direction,
   (b) the average speed for the whole journey.

41. The length of the sides of $\triangle ABC$ in cm are positive integers. BC is 12 cm longer than AB. CA is 28 cm longer than AB. Find the minimum perimeter of $\triangle ABC$.

42. An aptitude test has 30 questions in Section A and 20 questions in Section B. Each question carries 1 point. The percentage of questions Tim answered correctly in Section A is 60%. If he wants to obtain an overall percentage of questions answered correctly over 70%, find the number of questions he should answer correctly in Section B.

43. **(a)** Suppose that r is a positive rational number and $r > \sqrt{7}$. Show that $\dfrac{3r + 7}{r + 3}$ is closer to $\sqrt{7}$ than r is.
   (b) If $r = \dfrac{8}{3}$ is an initial approximation to $\sqrt{7}$, obtain two better approximations, as fractions, to $\sqrt{7}$ using the result in **(a)**.

Perimeters And Areas Of Plane Figures

Basic Practice

1. Find the area and perimeter of a square if the length of its side is
   (a) 7 cm,
   (b) x cm,
   (c) $6x$ cm.

2. Find the area and perimeter of a rectangle if its length and width are
   (a) 5 cm and 8 cm respectively,
   (b) 9 cm and $(2x + 3)$ cm respectively,
   (c) $3x$ cm and $(4x - 5)$ cm respectively.

3. Find, in terms of π, the area and circumference of a circle if its
   (a) radius is 4 cm,
   (b) radius is $5x$ cm,
   (c) diameter is 15 cm,
   (d) diameter is $6y$ cm.

4. Find the area of $\triangle ABC$ in each of the following figures. The unit of length is cm.

   (a)
   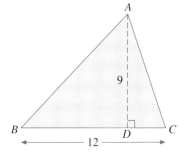

   (b)
   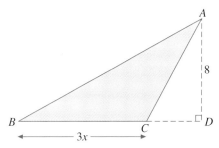

   (c)
   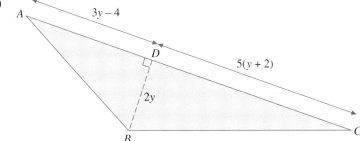

5. Find the value of x in each of the following figures. The unit of length is cm.

(a) Perimeter of square $ABCD$ = 8 cm

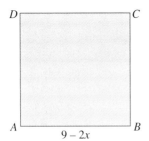

(b) Area of rectangle $PQRS$ = 50 cm^2

(c) Perimeter of $\triangle XYZ$ = 98 cm

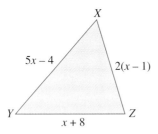

(d) Area of $\triangle DEF$ = 90 cm^2

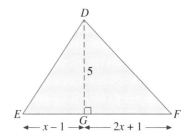

6. Find the area of the parallelogram $ABCD$ in each of the following figures. The unit of length is cm.

(a)

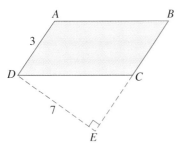

(b)

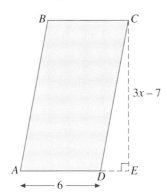

(c) $AECF$ is a square.

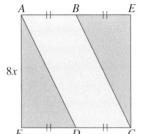

(d) $ABCD$ is a rhombus.

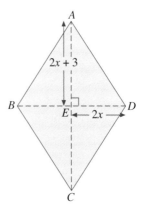

7. Find the area of the trapezoid *ABCD* in each of the following figures. The unit of length is cm.

(a)

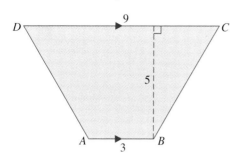

(b)

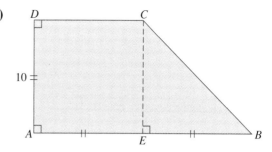

(c)

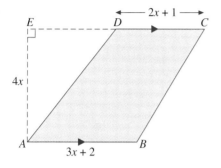

(d) *AECF* and *EDGC* are squares.

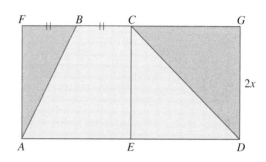

8. Find the value of *x* in each of the following figures if *ABCD* is a parallelogram. The unit of length is cm.

(a)

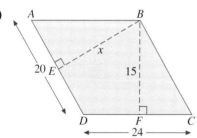

(b) Area of *ABCD* = 77 cm²

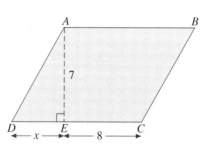

(c) Area of *ABCD* = 168 cm²

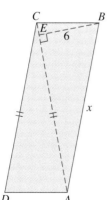

(d) *ABCD* is a rhombus.

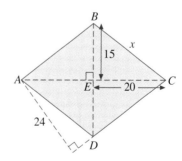

27

9. Find the perimeter and area of each of the following figures. The unit of length is cm.

(a)

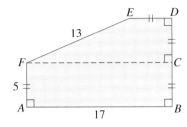

(b)

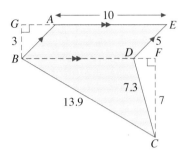

(c)

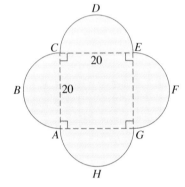

(d)

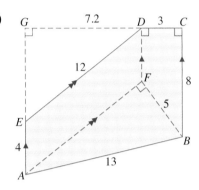

10. Find the perimeter and area of each of the following figures. The unit of length is cm.

(a)

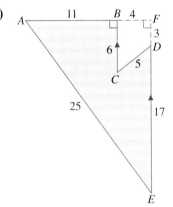

(b)

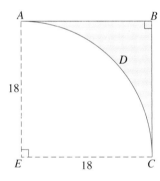

Take $\pi = 3.142$.

(c)

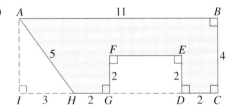

(d)

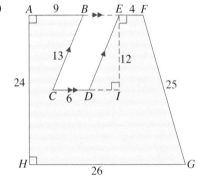

11. (a) A wire is bent into a square of area 81 cm². Find
    (i) the length of a side of the square,   **(ii)** the perimeter of the square.
  (b) Suppose the same wire is bent into an equilateral triangle. Find the length of a side of the equilateral triangle.

12. (a) The length and width of rectangle *ABCD* are 25 cm and 32 cm respectively. Find
    (i) the perimeter of the rectangle,   **(ii)** the area of the rectangle.
  (b) A square is formed when the sides of *ABCD* are extended. If the length of *ABCD* is extended by 60%, find
    (i) the length of the square,
    (ii) the percentage increase in the width of the rectangle.
  (c) Express the area of the square as a percentage of the area of the rectangle.

13. Two small circles are cut out from a large circle of diameter 48 cm. The point *O* is the center of the large circle and the diameters of the small circles are *OX* and *OY* respectively. The points *X* and *Y* are on the circumference of the large circle.
Find, in terms of π,
(a) the area of the resulting plane figure,
(b) the perimeter of the resulting plane figure.

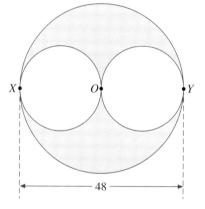

14. (a) Plot each of the following points in the given diagram.
    (i) *A*(–3, –4), *B*(2, –4), and *C*(4, 1)
    (ii) *P*(–4, 1), *Q*(–4, –2), and *R*(2, 3)
  (b) Hence, find the area of
    (i) △*ABC*,
    (ii) △*PQR*.
  (c) The points *D* and *S* lie on the *x*-axis and *y*-axis respectively. Find the area of
    (i) △*ABD*,
    (ii) △*PQS*.

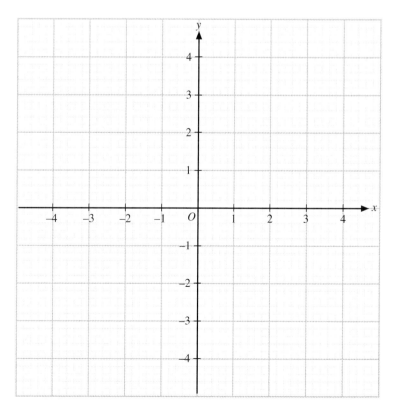

15. In the diagram, AE is parallel to BD and AC is parallel to ED. The point C lies on BD and $m\angle ABC = 90°$. The lengths of AB, AE, and DE are 24 cm, 20 cm, and 26 cm respectively.

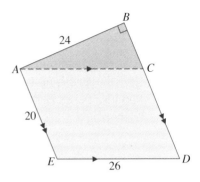

  (a) What type of quadrilateral is $ACDE$?
  (b) If the perimeter of the quadrilateral $ABDE$ is 100 cm, find
    (i) the length of BC,
    (ii) the area of $\triangle ABC$,
    (iii) the area of quadrilateral $ACDE$.
  (c) Given that the point F lies on DE and BF is perpendicular to DE, find the length of BF.

16. The diagram shows a sequence of figures formed by trapezoids. For each trapezoid, the lengths of the parallel sides are 6 cm and 10 cm respectively, the length of the base is 3 cm, and the length of the slanted side is 5 cm.

  (a) Draw the 5th figure.
  (b) Find the perimeter of the 5th figure.
  (c) Let the area of the nth figure be A_n cm^2.
    (i) Find A_1, A_2, A_3, and A_4.
    (ii) Express A_n in terms of n.
  (d) Hence, find the area of the 15th figure.

17. In the diagram, AC and AF are parallel to FD and BE respectively, B and E lie on AC and FD respectively, and the lines BE and CF meet at the point G. The line CD is perpendicular to the line FD. If $DE : DF : CA = 2 : 5 : 9$, find

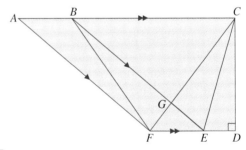

  (a) area of $\triangle CDE$: area of $\triangle EBF$,
  (b) area of $\triangle BCE$: area of $\triangle ABF$,
  (c) area of $\triangle CEF$: area of quadrilateral $ABEF$,
  (d) area of quadrilateral $BCDF$: area of quadrilateral $ABEF$.

18. A regular hexagon $ABCDEF$ is inscribed in a circle of diameter 16 cm. The point G is on the line FC, $m\angle CGD = 90°$, and $DG = 6.93$ cm.

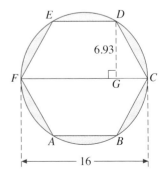

  (a) What type of quadrilateral is $ABCF$?
  (b) Find the perimeter of quadrilateral $ABCF$.
  (c) Find the area of quadrilateral $ABCF$.
  (d) Find the area of the shaded region.

19. In the diagram, *ABCD* is a rectangle of length 40 cm and width 10 cm, *AT* = *TQ*, *AP* = *PD*, *DS* = *SC*, and *m*∠*APR* = *m*∠*AQS* = 90°.

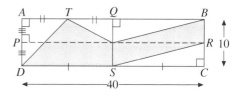

(a) Find the area of the shaded region.

(b) Express the area of the shaded region as a percentage of the area of rectangle *ABCD*.

20. 6 circles are cut off and removed from a rectangular piece of paper. These circles touch the sides of the paper at the points *A* to *J* as shown. The radius of each circle is 8 cm.

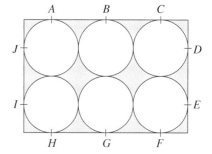

(a) Find the length and width of the paper.

(b) Find the area of the quadrilateral *ABEI*.

(c) Find

    (i) the area of the paper that remains,

    (ii) the perimeter of the paper that remains.

Challenging Practice

21. In the figure, *AB* is parallel to *CD* and *EF* is parallel to *GH*. The line *AB* meets the lines *EF* and *GH* at *P* and *Q* respectively. The line *CD* meets the line *GH* at *R*. Show, stating reasons, the area of △*PCQ* is equal to the area of △*QRF*.

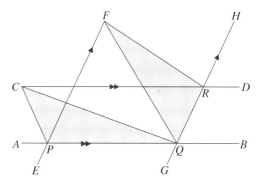

22. The figure shows a cross sectional view of the track of a tank. *AFE* and *BDC* are semicircles and the lengths of *AE* and *AB* are 0.9 m and 5.5 m respectively.

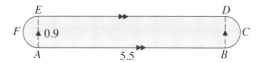

(a) Find the

    (i) perimeter of the track,

    (ii) area of the track.

(b) The tank moves at an average speed of 40 km/hr for 15 minutes. Find the distance covered by the tank.

(c) Let the number of revolutions made by the track in 15 minutes be *x*.

    (i) Form an equation in terms of *x* and solve it.

    (ii) Hence, find the number of complete revolutions made by the track.

23. (a) Plot each of the following points in the given diagram.

    (i) $A(-6, -15)$,   **(ii)** $B(8, -9)$,

    (iii) $C(2, 12)$,   **(iv)** $D(-8, 5)$.

(b) Find the area of $\triangle ABC$.

(c) Find the area of the quadrilateral $ABCD$.

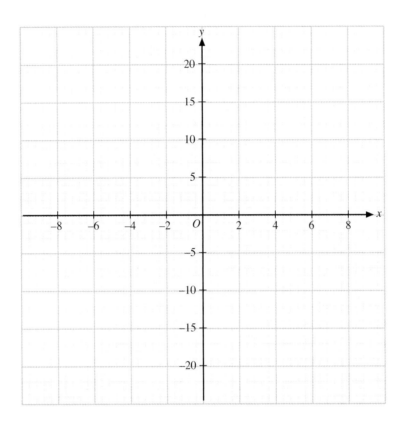

24. A parallelogram, a square, a triangle, and a trapezoid are fitted together to form the figure shown. The length of a side of the square is 6 cm, $AB = CD = (x + 1)$ cm, and the height of the trapezoid is 2 cm.

(a) Express, in terms of x, the area of the trapezoid.

(b) Show that the area of the parallelogram is twice the area of the triangle.

(c) Express, in terms of x, the area of the figure.

(d) The area of the square is $\dfrac{4}{9}$ the area of the figure.

    (i)   Form an equation in terms of x and solve it.

    (ii) Hence, find the area of the trapezoid.

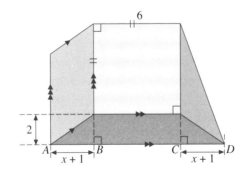

25. The length and width of a rectangular art paper are 60 cm and 45 cm respectively. The paper is folded at the two corners on the top and a semicircle of diameter 14 cm is cut off from the bottom as shown in the diagram.
   (a) Find the perimeter of the shaded region.
   (b) Find the area of the shaded region.

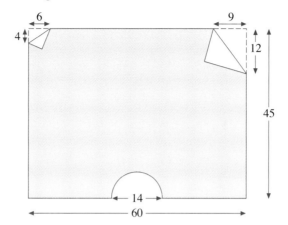

Enrichment

26. In the diagram, $ABCD$ is a straight line, $AB = 10$ cm, $BC = 15$ cm, and $CD = 7$ cm. $ABIJ$, $BCGH$, and $CDEF$ are squares. Find the area of $\triangle DFJ$.

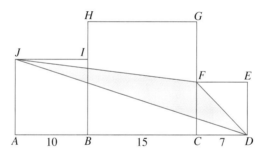

27. In figures 27*a* and 27*b*, I, II, III, IV are four identical right-angled triangles. They are arranged to form the shapes $ABCD$ in fig. 27*a* and $PQRS$ in fig. 27*b*. In $\triangle ABE$, $AB = 17$ cm and $AE - BE = 7$ cm.
   (a) Explain briefly why $ABCD$ is a square and find its area.
   (b) Explain briefly why $EFGH$ is a square and find its area.
   (c) Find the area of $\triangle ABE$.
   (d) Explain briefly why $PQRS$ is a square and find its area.

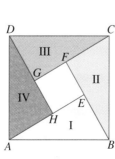

Fig. 27*a*

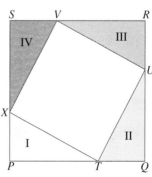

Fig. 27*b*

28. In the diagram, two parallelograms *ABCD* and *PQRS* overlap in a smaller parallelogram *PECF*. The area of *ABCD* is 180 cm² and the area of $PECF = \frac{1}{4} \times$ area of $ABCD = \frac{1}{6} \times$ area of *PQRS*.

   (a) Find the total area of the diagram.
   (b) If *AB* = 18 cm, find the height from *D* to *AB*.

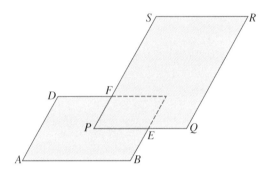

29. The diagram is bounded by 4 semicircles whose diameters are on the line segment *ABCD*. It is given that *AC* = 10 cm and *BD* = 18 cm. Find the enclosed area of the diagram.

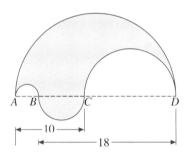

13 Volumes And Surface Areas Of Solids

Basic Practice

1. Find the volume and the total surface area of a cube whose side is
   (a) 4 cm,
   (b) 7.5 cm,
   (c) $\frac{1}{2}$ cm,
   (d) $\frac{3}{4}$ cm,
   (e) x cm,
   (f) $2x$ cm.

2. Find the volume and the total surface area of a cuboid whose dimensions are
   (a) 5 cm by 6 cm by 4 cm,
   (b) 8 cm by 4.5 cm by 3 cm,
   (c) 3.5 cm by 4.5 cm by 12 cm,
   (d) 7 cm by 3 cm by x cm,
   (e) $(x + 1)$ cm by 2 cm by 3 cm,
   (f) x cm by $2x$ cm by 1 cm,
   (g) x cm by y cm by 1 cm,
   (h) $2x$ cm by $3y$ cm by 2 cm.

3. (a) Find the volume and the total surface area of a solid cube whose side is 16 cm.
   (b) The solid cube is cut into 8 small cubes of equal volume. Find the
      (i) length of the side of each small cube,
      (ii) sum of the surface areas of the 8 small cubes.
   (c) Find the percentage change in the total surface area after the solid cube is cut into 8 small cubes.

4. Find the volume and total surface area of each prism. The unit of measurement is cm.

   (a)
   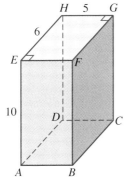

   (b)
   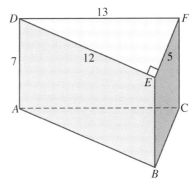

   (c)
   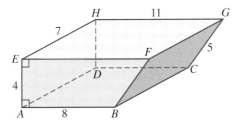

   (d)
   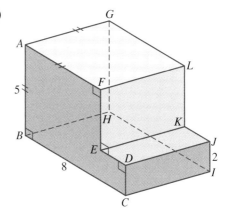

5. The figure on the right shows a prism. The unit of measurement is cm. Find
   (a) the volume of the prism,
   (b) the total surface area of the prism.

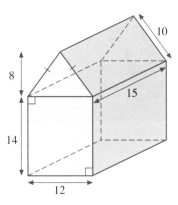

6. The figure shows a triangular prism in which $AB = AC = 17$ cm, $AJ = 15$ cm, $BC = 16$ cm, $CF = 25$ cm, and $m\angle AJB = 90°$.
   (a) Find the volume and total surface area of the triangular prism.
   (b) Two smaller prisms are formed when the prism is cut along a cross-section GHI. Find the sum of the surface areas of the two prisms.
   (c) Find the percentage change in the total surface area after the solid prism is cut into 2 smaller prisms.

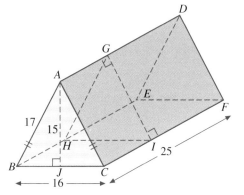

7. Figure A shows an open rectangular container $STUVWXYZ$ which is $\frac{4}{5}$ filled with water. The internal dimensions of the container are 75 cm long, 25 cm wide, and 45 cm high. The base, $STUV$, of the container is resting on a flat surface.

   In Figure B, the container is tilted about the edge SV and some water has been poured out.

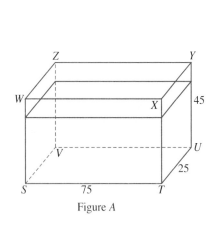

Figure A

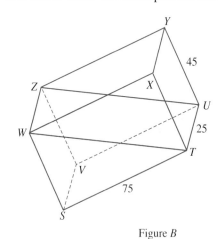

Figure B

   (a) Find the depth of the water in Figure A.
   (b) Find the volume of the water in Figure A.
   (c) Express the volume of water poured out in Figure B as a percentage of the volume of water in Figure A.

8. **(a)** Express the following areas in m².
   (i) 50,000 cm²
   (iii) 8,320 cm²
   (ii) 7,456,000 cm²
   (iv) 63 cm²
   (b) Express the following areas in cm².
   (i) 6 m²
   (ii) 9.4 m²
   (iii) 0.03 m²
   (iv) $\frac{7}{8}$ m²

9. **(a)** Express the following volumes in m³.
   (i) 2,000,000 cm³
   (iii) 600 cm³
   (ii) 345,000 cm³
   (iv) 25 cm³
   (b) Express the following volumes in cm³.
   (i) 3 m³
   (ii) 4.5 m³
   (iii) 0.1 m³
   (iv) $\frac{1}{4}$ m³

10. The internal dimensions of a rectangular tank are 75 cm long, 45 cm wide, and 40 cm high. If the tank is $\frac{2}{5}$ filled with water, find
   (a) the depth of the water,
   (b) the volume of the water
   (i) in cm³,
   (ii) in m³,
   (c) the total surface area of the tank that is in contact with the water
   (i) in cm²,
   (ii) in m².

(**Further Practice**)────────────────────────────

11. **(a)** Find the total surface area of a cube if the length of its side is 12 cm.
   (b) The dimensions of a cuboid are 15 cm by 7 cm by x cm and its total surface area is 50 cm² more than that of the cube in **(a)**.
   (i) Form an equation in terms of x and solve it.
   (ii) Hence, find the volume of the cuboid.

12. The dimensions of the base of a solid cuboid are 14 cm by x cm and the perimeter of the base is 80 cm.
   (a) Find
   (i) the value of x,
   (ii) the area of the base.
   (b) Find the height of the cuboid if the total surface area of the cuboid is 5 times the area of the base.
   (c) Find the volume of the cuboid in **(b)**.

13. The figure shows two cubes of sides 2 cm and 5 cm respectively.
   (a) Find the volume of the figure.
   (b) Find the total surface area of the figure.

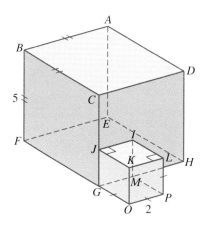

14. The figure shows a net of a prism.
The unit of measurement is cm.
  (a) Name the prism.
  (b) Find
    (i) the perimeter of the net,
    (ii) the total surface area of the prism,
    (iii) the volume of the prism.

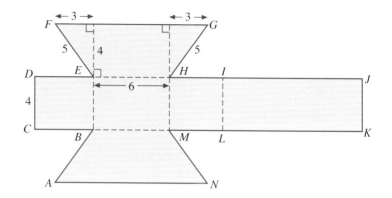

15. (a) Draw a net of the solid shown.
  (b) Hence, find the total surface area of the solid.
  (All dimensions in the diagram are in centimeters.)

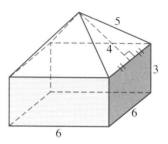

16. Find the volume and total surface area of each prism. The unit of measurement is cm.

(a)

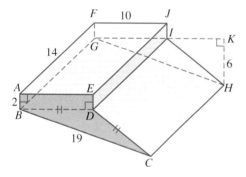

(b)

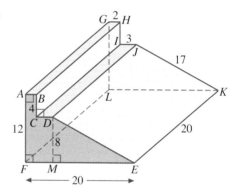

(c)

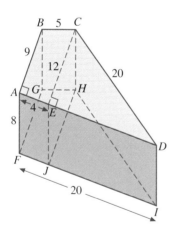

(d)

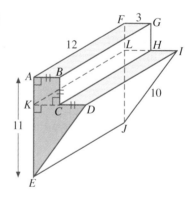

17. Find the volume and total surface area of the prism.
The unit of measurement is cm.

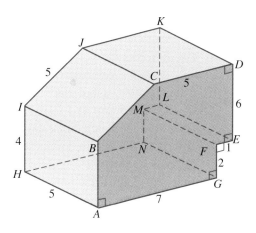

18. The figure shows a prism in which the height $AE = 25$ cm, $AB = 8.5$ cm, $BC = 13$ cm, $CD = 3x$ cm, and $AD = 4x$ cm.
 (a) If the volume of the prism is 4,500 cm^3, find the area of $ABCD$.
 (b) The area of $ADHE$ is 125 cm^2 more than that of $CDHG$.
     Form an equation in terms of x and solve it.
 (c) Hence, find the total surface area of the prism.

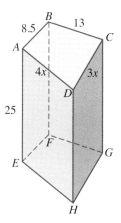

19. The figure shows the uniform cross-section of a solid crystal prism. $AB = 3$ cm, $BC = DC = 5$ cm, $CI = 3$ cm, $BD = 8$ cm, $AJ = JH = FG = 1.5$ cm, and $EF = 3.5$ cm. The thickness of the crystal prism is 6 cm.

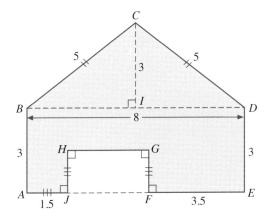

Find
 (a) the volume of the crystal prism,
 (b) the total surface area of the crystal prism,
 (c) the cost of the prism if every cm^3 of the crystal costs 85 cents,
 (d) the cost of polishing the prism if it costs 10 cents to polish every cm^2.

20. The internal dimensions of an open rectangular container are 36 cm long, 26 cm wide, and x cm high. The internal volume of the container is 0.06084 m³.
   (a) **(i)** Express the volume of the container in cm³.
       (ii) Find the value of x.
   (b) Candles with square bases are to be placed inside the container. The base area and height of each candle are 25 cm² and x cm respectively.
       (i) Find the volume of each candle.
       (ii) Find the maximum number of candles that can be placed inside the container.
   (c) Suppose the candles in **(b)(ii)** are first melted into liquid wax and then poured into the container. Find, correct to 2 decimal places, the depth of the liquid wax. Assume that the difference in volumes between the same quantity of solid and liquid wax is negligible.

(**Challenging Practice**)

21. Find the volume of the solid below. All dimensions given in the diagram are in meters.

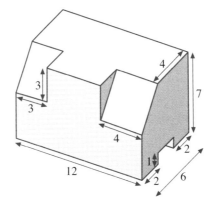

22. The internal dimensions of an open rectangular container are 80 cm long, 40 cm wide, and 36 cm high.
   (a) If the container is filled with 102,400 cm³ of water, find
       (i) the depth of the water in the container,
       (ii) the ratio of the volume of water to that of the container.
   (b) The depth of the water increases by 5% when 10 identical solid metal cubes are dropped into the container. Find
       (i) the rise in the water level,
       (ii) the total volume of the 10 cubes,
       (iii) the sum of the surface areas of the 10 cubes.

23. The figure shows an empty container with a pentagonal base. The base area and the height of the container are 1,250 cm² and 30 cm respectively. A metal cuboid of dimensions 20 cm long, $(x + 2)$ cm wide, and $(2y - 3)$ cm high is placed inside the container. The volume of the cuboid is 960 cm³.
   (a) Find the volume of the container
       (i) in cm³,
       (ii) in m³.

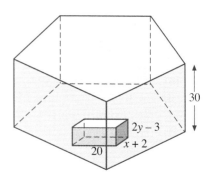

(b) 6,540 cm³ of water is poured into the container to just submerge the cuboid. Find
   (i) the height of the cuboid,
   (ii) the width of the cuboid,
   (iii) the total surface area of the cuboid.
(c) Hence, find the values of x and y.

24. A swimming pool is 100 m long and 40 m wide. The bottom of the pool slopes uniformly throughout the length of the pool. It is 1.75 m deep at the shallow end and 3 m deep at the deep end. The depth of water at the shallow end is 1 m.
(a) Find the volume of water in the pool in m³.
(b) How much more water must be poured into the pool to fill it completely?
(c) It takes 30 seconds to drain 10 m³ of water. Find the total time, in hours and minutes, needed to drain a fully filled pool.

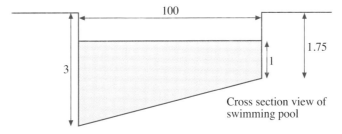

Cross section view of swimming pool

25. The diagram shows a sequence of figures formed by stacking solid cubes together. The volume of each cube is 1 cm³.

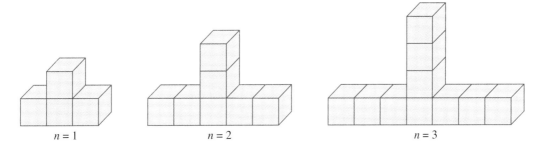

$n = 1$ $n = 2$ $n = 3$

Let the volume and total surface area of the cubes in the nth figure be V_n cm³ and A_n cm² respectively.
(a) Complete the following table.

n	1	2	3
V_n	4		
A_n		30	42

(b) Find an expression for
   (i) V_n,
   (ii) A_n.
(c) Hence, show that
   (i) the total surface area of the cubes in any figure is divisible by 6,
   (ii) $4V_n = A_n - 2$.
(d) The total surface area of all the cubes in the pth figure is 102 cm². Find
   (i) the corresponding volume of the cubes,
   (ii) the value of p.

26. In the diagram, three cubical building blocks are stacked up on a table. The lengths of the sides of the blocks are 5 cm, 10 cm, and 15 cm respectively.

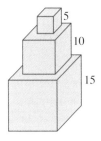

    (a) Find the total area of the exposed surfaces of the stack, excluding the contact surface with the table.

    (b) If a cylinder of height 30 cm has volume equal to the total volume of the blocks, find the base radius of the cylinder.

27. Six cubes of side 1 cm are glued together to form a solid. Three possible solids *P*, *Q*, and *R* are shown below.

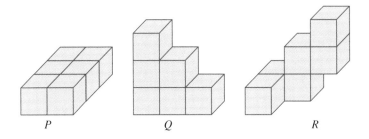

    (a) Determine the total surface area of solid
        (i) *P*,
        (ii) *Q*,
        (iii) *R*.
    (b) Form a solid with the least total surface area.
    (c) Form a solid with the greatest total surface area.

28.

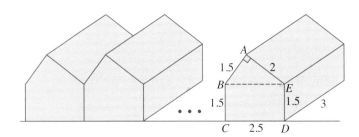

A developer builds a row of identical semi-detached huts along a beach as shown in the diagram above. *ABCDE* is the cross-section of a hut. $\triangle ABE$ is a right-angled triangle with $AB = 1.5$ m, $AE = 2$ m, and $m\angle BAE = 90°$. *BCDE* is a rectangle with $CD = 2.5$ m and $BC = 1.5$ m. The length of each hut is 3 m. The thickness of each side wall is 30 cm.

    (a) Find the total surface area of each hut, excluding the floor.

    (b) Find the volume of space of each hut (ignore the thickness of the walls).

    (c) If *n* huts are in a row, find, in terms of *n*,
        (i) the total roof area,
        (ii) the total volume of the side walls.

14 Proportions

Basic Practice

1. Express each of the following scales in the form 1 : r.
   - (a) 1 in. : 5 ft
   - (b) 1 in. : 4 yd
   - (c) 5 ft : 1 mi
   - (d) 32 yd : 1 mi
   - (e) 3 cm : 600 m
   - (f) 4 cm : 500 m
   - (g) 8 cm : 3.2 km
   - (h) 0.2 cm : 0.04 km

2. The scale of a map is $\frac{1}{250,000}$. Find the actual distance, in km, for each of the following distances on the map.
   - (a) 1 cm
   - (b) 6 cm
   - (c) 0.8 cm
   - (d) 2.5 cm
   - (e) 30 mm
   - (f) 45 mm

3. The scale of a map is 1 : 50,000. Find the distance on the map, in cm, for each of the following actual distances.
   - (a) 1 km
   - (b) 6 km
   - (c) 0.75 km
   - (d) 3.5 km
   - (e) 800 m
   - (f) 1,900 m

4. The scale of a map is $\frac{1}{40,000}$. Find the actual area, in km^2, for each of the following areas on the map.
   - (a) 1 cm^2
   - (b) 15 cm^2
   - (c) 0.6 cm^2
   - (d) 9.5 cm^2
   - (e) 500 mm^2
   - (f) 8,000 mm^2

5. The scale of a map is 1 : 20,000. Find the area on the map, in cm^2, for each of the following actual areas.
   - (a) 1 km^2
   - (b) 4 km^2
   - (c) 0.7 km^2
   - (d) 5.6 km^2
   - (e) 60,000 m^2
   - (f) 1,500,000 m^2

6. It is given that y is directly proportional to x. When $x = 3$, $y = 18$.
   - (a) Find the equation connecting x and y.
   - (b) Hence, find
     - (i) the value of y when $x = 12$,
     - (ii) the value of x when $y = 42$.

7. It is given that V is directly proportional to r^3. When $r = 4$, $V = 32$.
   (a) Find the equation connecting r and V.
   (b) Hence, find
       (i) the value of V when $r = 5$,
       (ii) the value of r when $V = 108$.

8. It is given that q is inversely proportional to p. When $p = 6$, $q = 16$.
   (a) Find the equation connecting p and q.
   (b) Hence, find
       (i) the value of q when $p = 3$,
       (ii) the value of p when $q = 8$.

9. It is given that C is inversely proportional to b^2 and $b > 0$. When $b = \dfrac{1}{2}$, $C = 40$.

   (a) Find the equation connecting b and C.
   (b) Hence, find
       (i) the value of C when $b = 5$,
       (ii) the value of b when $C = \dfrac{1}{10}$.

10. Two quantities, v and $\sqrt{w}$, are connected by the equation $v = k\sqrt{w}$. The table below shows some values of v and w.

w	4	25	b
v	4	a	16

Find the value of
(a) k,
(b) a,
(c) b.

(**Further Practice**)

---

11. The scale of a map is 2 cm : 500 m.

   (a) Express the scale in the form $\dfrac{1}{r}$.

   (b) A rectangle of length 8 cm and width 5.5 cm is drawn on the map. Calculate
       (i) the actual perimeter of the rectangle in km,
       (ii) the actual area of the rectangle in km^2.

12. Suppose that every 4 cm on a map represents an actual length of 1 km.
   (a) Express the scale of the map in the form $1 : r$.
   (b) If the distance between 2 schools on the map is 9.5 cm, find their actual distance apart in km.
   (c) If the actual distance between a cinema and a park is 15 km, find their distance apart on the map in mm.

13. A straight road, 2 km long, is represented by a 4 cm line on map A and a 5 cm line on map B.
   (a) Express, in the form $1 : r$, the scale of
      (i)   map A,
      (ii) map B.
   (b) The scale of map C is $1 : 10,000$. Calculate the length of the road on map C.

14. The scale of map P is $\dfrac{1}{p}$ and the scale of map Q is $\dfrac{1}{q}$. Suppose a street is represented by lines of 12 cm long and 16 cm long on maps P and Q respectively.
   (a) Find $\dfrac{p}{q}$ and express the answer in the simplest form.
   (b) If $p = 5,000$, find
      (i)   the value of q,
      (ii) the actual length, in m, of the street.
   (c) If $p = 5,000$ and the actual area of a plot of land is $2,812.5$ m^2, calculate its area on
      (i)   map P,
      (ii) map Q.

15. The mass, m grams, of a ball is directly proportional to its volume, V cm^3, which in turn is directly proportional to the cube of its radius, r cm. When m is $4,312$, V and r are $1,437\frac{1}{3}$ and 7 respectively.
   (a) Find the equation connecting
      (i) m and V,
      (ii) V and r,
      (iii) m and r.
   (b) Hence, calculate
      (i)   the mass of the ball if its radius is 2 cm,
      (ii) the radius of the ball if its mass is 539 g.

16. Some corresponding values of x and y are shown in the table for $1 \leqslant x \leqslant 5$.

x	1	2	3	4	5
y	5	8	11	14	17

   (a) **(i)** Draw the graph of y against x.
         (ii) Is y directly proportional to x? Explain your answer.
   (b) **(i)** Draw, on the same diagram, the graph of $(y - 2)$ against x.
         (ii) Is $(y - 2)$ directly proportional to x? Explain your answer.
   (c) **(i)** Find an equation connecting $(y - 2)$ and x.
         (ii) Hence, express y in terms of x.

17. Some corresponding values of x and y are shown in the table below.

x	2	3	5	11
y	100	50	25	10

   (a) Is y inversely proportional to x? Explain your answer.
   (b) Is y inversely proportional to $(x - 1)$? Explain your answer.
   (c) **(i)** Find an equation connecting $(x - 1)$ and y.
         (ii) Hence, find the value of x when $y = 5$.

18. It is given that $\sqrt{x}$ and y are in direct proportion. If the difference in the values of y when $x = 25$ and when $x = 4$ is 42, find
    (a) an equation connecting x and y,
    (b) the value of y when $x = 64$,
    (c) the value of x when $y = 98$.

19. Two quantities, x and y, are in inverse proportion. If the sum of the values of y when $x = 2$ and when $x = 8$ is 50, find
    (a) an equation connecting x and y,
    (b) the value of y when $x = 50$,
    (c) the value of x when $y = 1.25$.

20. Two quantities, p and q^2, are in inverse proportion. If the difference in the values of p when $q = 2$ and when $q = 10$ is 24, find
    (a) an equation connecting p and q,
    (b) the value of p when $q = 5$.

Challenging Practice

21. The scale of map X is $1 : x$ and the scale of map Y is $4 : y$. Suppose that the actual area of a park is represented by 10 cm^2 and 2.5 cm^2 on maps X and Y respectively.
    (a) Find $x : y$ and express the answer in the simplest form.
    (b) If $x = 50,000$, find
        (i) the value of y,
        (ii) the actual area of the park in km^2.
    (c) The length of a road on map X is 4 cm. Find
        (i) the actual length of the road,
        (ii) the length of the road on map Y.

22. A group of farmers works everyday at a constant rate to clear some land for planting crops. In the first 8 days, the land area cleared was represented by map A. After the first 8 days, the land area (inclusive of those in the first 8 days) cleared was represented by map B. The scales of maps A and B are $1 : x$ and $1 : y$ respectively. Find $x : y$ if the land areas cleared after 1 week and after 20 days were represented by 89.6 cm^2 and 100 cm^2 respectively.

23. The time taken to complete a school project is inversely proportional to the number of students involved. A team of 5 students can complete the project in 6 weeks.
    (a) Find the additional number of students needed if the project must be completed 12 days earlier.
    (b) Suppose that 4 weeks into the project, one of the 5 students left the team. The remaining students decide to continue with the project by themselves. Calculate the number of days needed to complete the project in this case.

24. Two quantities, E and c^2, are in direct proportion. It is known that $E = 5$ for a particular value of c.
  (a) Find the value of E when the value of c is
  (i) increased by 100%,
  (ii) increased by 200%,
  (iii) decreased by 50%.
  (b) Hence, calculate the corresponding percentage changes in the values of E for **(a)(i)** to **(a)(iii)**.

25. Two quantities, p and q^3, are in inverse proportion. It is known that $p = 540$ for a particular value of q.
  (a) Find the value of p when the value of q is
  (i) increased by 100%,
  (ii) increased by 200%,
  (iii) decreased by 50%.
  (b) Hence, calculate the corresponding percentage changes in the values of q for **(a)(i)** to **(a)(iii)**.

Enrichment

26. The cost of making an iron ball is directly proportional to the cube of the radius of the ball. It is given that the cost of making an iron ball of radius 4 cm is $160.
  (a) Find the cost of making an iron ball of radius 5 cm.
  (b) A ball of radius 4 cm is sold for $200. A ball of radius 5 cm is sold for $375. Which ball has a higher percentage profit on cost?

27. The figure shows a rectangular brick which is 24 cm long, 12 cm wide, and 7.5 cm high. When the brick is placed on the floor, the pressure acting on the floor is inversely proportional to the area of contact with the brick. When the brick is placed on the floor with face X in contact with the floor, the pressure is 375 units.

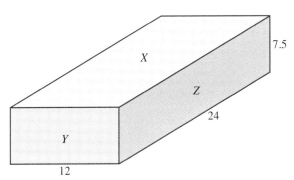

  (a) Find the pressure acting on the floor when the brick is placed on the floor with
  (i) face Y,
  (ii) face Z,
  in contact with the floor.
  (b) Find the maximum pressure that can act on the floor using 4 of these bricks.

28. The height of a TV set is directly proportional to its length.
   (a) Show that the screen area of the TV set is directly proportional to the square of its length.
   (b) When the length of the TV set is 80 cm, its height is 45 cm. If the length of the TV set is 120 cm, find its screen area.
   (c) Suggest the proportion relationship between the length of a diagonal of the TV set and its screen area.

29. On a map of scale $1 : 2r$, the length of a road is 15 cm and the area of a region is 36 cm^2.
   (a) Find the length of the road and the area of the region on a map of scale $1 : 3r$.
   (b) If the length of the road on another map is 24 cm, find the scale of that map in terms of r.

15 Data Handling

1. Helena wanted to determine whether a die was biased or not. She tossed the die 120 times and recorded the results.
   (a) What kind of data-collection method did she use?
   (b) What are the possible results in each toss?

2. The following dot plot shows the amount of money (to the nearest dollar) that a group of students had after recess on a particular school day.

Dot plot for the amount of money (nearest $) students had after recess

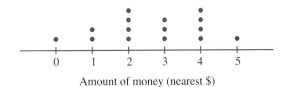

Amount of money (nearest $)

   (a) How many students were surveyed?
   (b) How many students had at most $3 after the recess?
   (c) Describe briefly the distribution of the data.

3. The following dot plot shows the number of A's students earned on all tests by the end of the year.

Dot plot for the number of A's earned

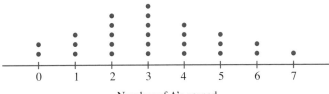

Number of A's earned

   (a) How many students are in the class?
   (b) How many students scored at most 2 A's?
   (c) How many students scored at least 1 A?
   (d) Describe briefly the distribution of the data.

4. (a) Find the mean of each of the following set of numbers.
   (i) 1, 5, 8, 16, 20
   (ii) 8, 6, 10, 21, 23, 4
   (iii) 4.4, 2.8, 9.5, 7.3
   (iv) −14, −5, −11, 2, 7, 21
   (v) −25, −14, −17, −33, 40, 9, 5
   (vi) $2x, 3x, 6x, 4x, 5x$
   (vii) $y, 3y + 3, 5y + 5, 3y − 2, 3y − 6$
   (viii) $15w, 12 − w, 14 − 4w, 3 − 3w, 11 − 7w$

(b) Calculate the mean absolute deviation (MAD) for each of the sets of numbers in **(a)(i)** to **(a)(iii)**.

5. The heights (in cm) of a group of 8 boys and a group of 8 girls in a class are given as follows.

Heights of boys (cm)	152	154	153	160	155	148	162	164
Heights of girls (cm)	144	153	147	161	149	150	165	147

(a) Find the mean and the mean absolute deviation (MAD) of the heights of
   (i) the group of boys,
   (ii) the group of girls.
(b) On average, which group is taller?
(c) In which group is there greater variation in heights?

6. Find the median of each of the following sets of numbers.
   (a) 10, 15, 23, 46, 55
   (b) 4, 15, 22, 36, 41, 50, 69
   (c) 12, 18, 27, 31, 49, 71
   (d) 7, 19, 21, 35, 68, 79, 98, 150
   (e) 67, 39, 23, 47, 100, 134, 81
   (f) 24, 102, 66, 9, 234, 77
   (g) $w − 5, w + 4, w − 10, w + 11, w − 1$
   (h) $3w − 12, 3w + 20, 3w − 20, 3w + 30$

7. The top speeds (to the nearest km/hr) of 16 cars are listed below. The median speed of the 16 cars is 198 km/hr.

166	173	179	182	186	192	195	195
x	208	215	221	227	232	235	252

(a) Find the value of x.
(b) Hence, find the mean of the data.

8. Find the mode of each of the following sets of numbers where possible.
   (a) 7, 8, 14, 25, 42, 7, 23, 7
   (b) 15, 74, 55, 46, 15, 74, 61, 74
   (c) 101, 58, 76, 101, 58, 39, 46
   (d) 24, 102, 66, 9, 234, 77
   (e) $2w, 6w, 4w, w, 5w, 2w, 3w$
   (f) $w + 4, 2w + 7, 2w − 7, 4 + w, 2x − 7, 2x + 7$

9. Find the mean, median, and mode of x in the following distributions.

(a)

6	2	4	6	2
2	0	0	2	2
2	4	2	0	6

(b)

3	1	2	4	1	2	2	5	5	5
2	2	3	1	1	2	3	5	5	3
3	2	2	3	2	4	5	3	4	5

(c)

−2	1	0	0	1	1	0	0	0	1
2	−2	−1	0	−2	−2	−2	−1	−1	1
−2	−2	−2	−2	−2	−2	−2	−1	−1	−1
2	2	−2	0	0	0	−1	−1	−2	2

10. The mean of the numbers 7, 24, 13, 18, 18, 24, 16, and x is 18.
  (a) Find the value of x.
  (b) Hence, find the mean absolute deviation (MAD) of the numbers.
  (c) State the mode of the numbers.
  (d) Find the median of the numbers.

(Further Practice)

11. A teacher wants to find out the number of his seventh grade students who have birthdays falling in each of the 12 months. He collects the data in the following ways.
  (a) Checking the date of birth of each student in the class roster.
  (b) Asking the students to raise their hands if their birthdays fall within a certain month.
  (c) Designing a form and getting the students to fill in their birth dates and return the forms to him.
  Name the data-collection method used in each case.

12. Each student in a school was asked to sell 6 school concert tickets. The following dot plot shows the number of tickets held by a group of students one week after the tickets were issued to them.

Dot plot for the number of concert tickets held after one week

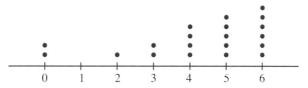

Number of concert tickets held after one week

  (a) How many students were in the group?
  (b) How many students have sold all the tickets after one week?
  (c) How many students have sold at least 4 tickets after one week?
  (d) Describe briefly the distribution of the data.

13. The following dot plot shows the number of windows in each of 16 rooms in a mansion.

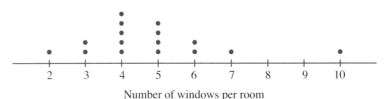

Dot plot for the number of windows per room

Number of windows per room

    (a) How many windows do most of the rooms have?
    (b) Find the percentage of rooms who have at least 6 windows.
    (c) How many windows do the 16 rooms have altogether?
    (d) Describe briefly the distribution of the data.

14. The dot plot shows the number of books owned by a group of students.

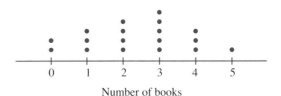

Number of books

    (a) How many students are in the group?
    (b) Find
        (i) the modal number of books owned,
        (ii) the median number of books owned,
        (iii) the mean number of books owned.
    (c) The mean number of books owned is 2.5 if two students are removed from the group. Calculate the total number of books these two students owned.

15. The number of days that each of 20 employees was on medical leave in a 6-month period is shown below:

1	2	5	0	3	4	5	3	2	1
2	5	2	4	1	2	0	4	0	2

    (a) Draw a dot plot to represent the above information.
    (b) Find
        (i) the mode of the distribution,
        (ii) the median of the distribution,
        (iii) the mean of the distribution.
    (c) Calculate the percentage of employees whose days on medical leave is more than the mean of the distribution.

16. The total expenses of 7 people in a particular month are $610, $730, $940, $650, $740, $850, and $660.
    (a) Find the mean monthly expenses of the 7 people.
    (b) The mean monthly expenses will become $755 if the monthly expenses of one of the 7 people is excluded. Calculate the monthly expenses of the excluded person.
    (c) The mean monthly expenses will become $760 if the monthly expenses of an 8th person is included in the data set. Calculate the monthly expenses of the 8th person.

17. The number of books read by a group of students during the summer break is tabulated below.

Number of books read	0	1	2	3	4	5	6	7
Number of students	2	3	4	x	3	8	5	2

(a) Find the value of x if the median number of books read is 4.5.
(b) Find the number of students in the group.
(c) Calculate the mean number of books read.

18. The values of 5 numbers are $z - 4$, $z - 4$, $z + 2$, $z + 5$, $z + 7$.
(a) Find the value of z if the median of the numbers is twice the mode.
(b) Hence, find the mean of the numbers.

19. (a) Arrange the numbers $(w - 9)$, $(w + 10)$, $(w - 15)$, $(w + 5)$, $(w - 3)$, and $(w + 6)$ in ascending order.
(b) (i) Find the median of the numbers in terms of w.
(ii) Find the value of w if the median of the numbers is 20.
(c) Hence, calculate the mean of the numbers.

20. The number of movies that a group of adults watched during a one-month period is tabulated below.

Number of movies watched	0	1	2	3	4	5	6
Number of adults	2	7	6	x	4	2	1

(a) Find the minimum value of x if the mode is 3.
(b) Using the value of x in (a), find
(i) the mean number of movies watched during the one-month period,
(ii) the median number of movies watched during the one-month period.

Challenging Practice

21. Two brands of smoked turkey breasts are sold in a supermarket at the same unit price. The masses, to the nearest gram, of the smoked turkey breasts are listed below.

Brand A

250	252	251	249	251	253
253	253	251	253	250	248

Brand B

247	250	248	251	254	255
251	254	251	253	249	250

(a) Draw dot plots to display the masses of each brand of smoked turkey breasts.
(b) Analyze and compare the two distributions.
(c) Find
(i) the mean,
(ii) the mean absolute deviation (MAD) of each distribution.
(d) The nominal mass of both brands of smoked turkey breasts is 250 g. How many smoked turkey breasts of each brand exceeded the nominal mass?
(e) Suppose that the qualities of both brands of smoked turkey breasts are the same. Choose the brand that is a better buy using the answers in (b), (c), and (d). Explain briefly your choice.

22. Whenever Jerome or Shernise is late for an appointment with a friend, each of them will send the short message "Late for 10 minutes" to the friend. The actual times (to the nearest minute) that they were late during 6 such occasions are listed in the following table.

Jerome (min)	8	11	9	15	x	16
Shernise (min)	17	10	$2x - 7$	13	6	7

(a) Suppose the means of the 2 sets of data are the same.
   (i) Find the value of x.
   (ii) Hence, find the mean of each set of data.
(b) Based on the answers in (a), should Jerome's or Shernise's friend wait for just 10 minutes whenever they are late? Explain your answer.
(c) Find the mean absolute deviation (MAD) for each set of data.
(d) Which set of data has a smaller variation?
(e) Suppose you are a friend of Jerome and Shernise. Based on your answer in (d), would you rather wait for Jerome or Shernise if they were late? Explain your answer.

23. The table below shows the number of passengers in each car that passes a particular police checkpoint.

Number of passengers	0	1	2	3	4
Number of cars	$x + 2$	8	10	9	$2x + 3$

Given that x is a positive integer, find
(a) the value of x if 65 cars pass the police checkpoint,
(b) the value of x if the mean number of passengers is 2.3,
(c) the maximum value of x if the modal number of passengers is not 4,
(d) the maximum and minimum values of x if the median number of passengers is 3.

24. The numbers '2', '4', '6', and '8' are printed on each card in a pack. The table below shows the number of each type of cards in terms of x.

Number on cards	2	4	6	8
Number of cards	$x - 3$	x	$x - 15$	$x - 9$

(a) Find the total number of cards in the pack in terms of x.
(b) State the mode of the data.
(c) Calculate the value of x if the mean, mode, and median are the same.
(d) Suppose that n cards that are printed with the number '6' are added to the pack.
   Find the maximum value of n if
   (i) the mode is unchanged,
   (ii) the median is unchanged.

25. The number of questions that are correctly answered by each student in a class in an 8-question quiz is tabulated below, where m, p, and q are non-negative integers.

Number of correctly answered questions	0	1	2	3	4	5	6	7	8
Number of students	3	4	7	m	p	q	9	2	1

(a) Find the value of m if the mean number of correct answers for all students who answered at most 3 questions correctly is 2.

(b) Show that $2p + q = 4$ if the mean number of correct answers for all students who answered at least 4 questions correctly is 6.

(c) Using your answers in (a) and (b), find the greatest possible number of students in the class.

Enrichment

26. Refer to the questionnaire below about a beverage to answer the following questions.

Customer Survey of *ABC* Drink

1. How many bottles do you drink in a week?

   1 ☐   2 ☐   3 ☐   4 ☐   5 ☐   6 ☐   7 ☐

2. How is the presentation of the package?

   Excellent ☐   Good ☐   Fair ☐   Poor ☐

3. What is the quality of the drink?

   _____

4. How did you learn about us?

   _____

5. Your name: _____

6. How old are you?

   15–30 ☐   31–50 ☐   51 or above ☐

(a) Is it necessary to ask a respondent to fill in his/her personal information, such as their name and age, in this questionnaire? Explain briefly.

(b) Which questions are difficult to analyze later on? Suggest some improvements.

(c) Comment on the way question 6 is phrased in the questionnaire.

(d) Draft an appropriate question to include in this questionnaire.

27. Mr. Scott is 41 years old. The mean age of Mr. and Mrs. Scott and their children is 21 years old. The mean age of Mrs. Scott and the children is 16 years old.
    (a) Find the number of children in the family.
    (b) Can you calculate Mrs. Scott's age from the given information? Explain briefly.
    (c) If the mean age of Mr. Scott and the children is 16.75 years old, find the age of Mrs. Scott.

28. There are four numbers a, b, c, and d. The mean of any 3 of them is added to the fourth number. The possible results are 22, 24, 28, and 34 respectively. Find the smallest of the original numbers.

29. The following dot plot shows the scores of some students in a test. The maximum number of points of the test is 10.

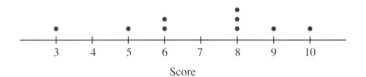

Score

    (a) Find the mean, median, and mode of the scores of the students.
    (b) If the lowest score is removed from the data set, describe the change in the mean, median, and mode. Which one of these measures is affected the most?

16 Probability Of Simple Events

Basic Practice

1. Represent each of the following sets by listing its elements.
   (a) A = {numbers on a standard die}
   (b) B = {faces on a coin}
   (c) C = {denominations of coins used in the United States}
   (d) E = {planets in the solar system}
   (e) F = {countries of Central America}

2. List the elements in each of the following sets.
   (a) $U = \{x: x$ is a factor of 20\}
   (b) $V = \{x: x$ is a common factor of 12 and 18\}
   (c) $W = \{x: x$ is a multiple of 4 that is less than 30\}
   (d) $X = \{x: x$ is a common multiple of 3 and 5 which is at most 60\}
   (e) $Y = \{x: x$ is a positive integer which satisfies the inequality $4x < 16$\}
   (f) $Z = \{x: x$ is a prime number that is less than 50\}

3. Find the set A' in each of the following cases.
   (a) ξ = {1, 3, 5, 8, 9, 12, 14} and A = {3, 5, 9, 12}
   (b) ξ = {b, d, h, i, j, m, p, q} and A = {b, h, i, j, q}
   (c) ξ = {red, green, blue, orange, yellow, purple} and A = {green, blue, yellow}
   (d) $\xi = \{x: x$ is an integer and $0 < x \leqslant 10\}$ and $A = \{x : x$ is a prime number\}
   (e) $\xi = \{x: x$ is a positive integer and x is divisible by 2\} and
       $A = \{x: x$ is a positive integer and x is divisible by 4\}
   (f) ξ = {letters in the word 'team'} and A = {letters in the word 'meat'}

4. Let ξ = {letters in the word 'singaporean'} and S = {letters in the word 'spring'}
   (a) List the elements in ξ and S.
   (b) List the elements in S'.
   (c) State $n(\xi)$, $n(S)$, and $n(S')$.

5. Let $\quad \xi$ = {banking, manufacturing, commerce, transport, construction},
   $\qquad A$ = {commerce, manufacturing, construction},
   and $\quad B$ = {transport, banking, commerce}.
   (a) List the elements of
       (i) A',
       (ii) B'.
   (b) What is the relationship between A and B'?

6. Let $\xi = \{2, 4, 6, 7, 8, 11, 16\}$, $P = \{2, 2^2, 2^3\}$, and $Q = \{4, \sqrt{4}, 4^2\}$.
   (a) (i) Is $P = Q$?   (ii) Is $n(P) = n(Q)$?
   (b) List the elements of
       (i) P',   (ii) Q'.

7. A bag contains 12 apples and 8 oranges. A fruit is selected at random from the bag. Find the probability of selecting
   (a) an apple,
   (b) an orange,
   (c) a pear.

8. A clip dispenser contains 50 clips, of which 10 are red clips and the rest are yellow clips. A clip is chosen at random from the dispenser. Find the probability of choosing
   (a) a red clip,
   (b) a yellow clip,
   (c) a clip which is red or yellow.

9. A letter is chosen at random from the word '*DISCOVERY*'. Find the probability that the letter chosen is
   (a) a '*V*',
   (b) found in the word '*LEGENDARY*',
   (c) not found in the word '*ORDINARY*'.

10. 18 movie DVDs and 14 game CDs are stored in a rack. $\frac{1}{3}$ of the movie DVDs are in English and the rest are in Spanish. A disc is selected at random from the rack.
    Find the probability of selecting
    (a) a movie DVD,
    (b) an English movie DVD,
    (c) a disc which is not a Spanish movie DVD.

11. A light bulb is randomly selected from a batch of 28 light bulbs, of which 7 are defective.
    (a) Find the probability of selecting
        (i) a defective light bulb,   (ii) a good light bulb.
    (b) Suppose that four defective bulbs are removed from the batch of 28 bulbs.
        Find the probability of selecting
        (i) a defective bulb from the remaining bulbs,
        (ii) a good bulb from the remaining bulbs.

12. A number is selected at random from all the prime numbers which are smaller than 30.
    (a) List the sample space.
    (b) Let W be the event that the number selected is at least 11.
        (i) Express W using the listing method.   (ii) Hence, find P(W) and P(W').

13. (a) List the sample space when all the letters from the word '*AIM*' are arranged from left to right in any order.
    (b) Let Q be the event that the middle letter is a vowel.
        (i) Express Q and Q' using the listing method.
        (ii) Hence, find P(Q) and P(Q').

14. A fair die has 8 faces, numbered 1 to 8. When it is tossed, find the probability of getting
  (a) an odd number,
  (b) a number greater than 5,
  (c) a prime number,
  (d) a number which is a factor of 48.

15. A card is selected at random from a set of 15 cards, numbered 6 to 20. Find the probability that the number on the card is
  (a) even,
  (b) a multiple of 3,
  (c) a factor of 30,
  (d) not a prime number.

16. In the diagram, *ABCD* is a rectangle. The points *E*, *F*, and *G*, on the perimeter of *ABCD* are such that *AE = BE* and *BF = CF* respectively.
A point within *ABCD* is randomly selected.
Find the probability of selecting a point in
  (a) △*CFG*,
  (b) △*BEF*,
  (c) the shaded region.

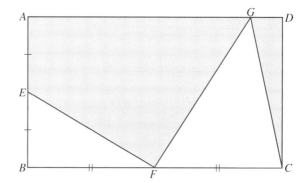

Further Practice

17. Suggest a universal set for each of the following sets.
  (a) {bus, taxi, bicycle, train, truck}
  (b) {printer, hard disk, monitor, keyboard, mouse}
  (c) {fork, knife, spoon, plate}
  (d) {corporal, sergeant, private, captain}
  (e) {10°, 24°, 43°, 65°}
  (f) {–5, 1, 7, 13, 20}

18. Let   *P* = {letters from the word 'estimates'},
              Q = {letters from the word 'mathematics'},
  and   *R* = {letters from the word 'meticulous'}.
  (a) (i) List the elements of *P*, *Q*, and *R*.
    (ii) State $n(P)$, $n(Q)$ and $n(R)$.
  (b) Determine whether each of the following statements is true or false.
    (i) $\{a, c, e, s\} \in Q$,
    (ii) $\phi \subset \{m\}$,
    (iii) $a \notin R$.
  (c) Let *S* = {letters from the word 'time'}. Describe the relationship between the sets
    (i) *P* and *S*,
    (ii) *Q* and *S*,
    (iii) *P* and *Q*.

19. Suppose that A and B are subsets of a universal set ξ.

Let $\quad \xi = \{x: x \text{ is an integer and } 1 \leqslant x \leqslant 12\}$,

$\qquad\quad A = \{x: 3x < 24\}$,

and $\quad B = \{x: 2x > 11\}$.

(a) List the elements of A and B.

(b) List the elements of A' and B'.

20. Let $\quad \xi = \{x: x \text{ is a positive integer and } x < 100\}$,

$\qquad\quad S = \{x: x \text{ is a positive 2-digit number and the sum of the 2 digits} = 9\}$,

and $\quad T = \{x: x \text{ is a multiple of 9}\}$.

(a) List the elements of S and T.

(b) Describe, using '$\subset$', the relationship between

$\quad$ **(i)** S and T,

$\quad$ **(ii)** S' and T'.

(c) Find $n(S')$ and $n(T')$ without listing their elements.

21. The frequency table below shows the lengths of service, in years, of 80 employees in a company.

Length of service (years)	2	3	4	5	6
Number of employees	w	19	$w + 1$	16	14

(a) Find the value of w.

(b) State the modal length of service.

(c) An employee is randomly selected to attend a briefing on safety at workplace.

Find the probability of selecting an employee who has been working in the company for

$\quad$ **(i)** 2 years,

$\quad$ **(ii)** at least 5 years,

$\quad$ **(iii)** more than 2 years but less than 5 years.

22. (a) Write one million, three hundred forty three thousand, six hundred, thirty-nine in numerical form.

(b) Each of the 7 digits that form the number in **(a)** is written on a card.

A card is then randomly selected. Find the probability of selecting a

$\quad$ **(i)** 3,

$\quad$ **(ii)** number greater than 5,

$\quad$ **(iii)** factor of 36.

23. A bag contains 60 balls of which x are red, y are blue, and the rest are green. A ball is randomly picked.

It is known that the probability of picking a red ball is $\dfrac{1}{4}$ and the probability of picking a green ball

is $\dfrac{7}{15}$.

(a) Form an equation in x.

(b) Form an equation in x and y.

(c) **(i)** Solve the equations in **(a)** and **(b)**.

$\qquad$ **(ii)** Hence, state the probability of picking a blue ball.

24. Number cards that are even are first removed from a set of cards numbered 1 to 43. Cards with numbers that are divisible by 3 are next removed from the cards that remain.
    (a) (i)   List the numbers on the cards that finally remain.
        (ii) Hence, state the number of cards that finally remain.
    (b) A card from (a) is picked randomly. Find the probability that the number on the card
        (i)   is a prime number,
        (ii) is a multiple of 5,
        (iii) has the digit '3'.

25. 5 students, Margaret (M), Vincent (V), John (J), Susan (S), and Raymond (R) are seated in a row such that the first and the last persons of the row are girls.
    (a) List the sample space.
    (b) Find the probability that John sits in the middle of the row.
    (c) Let A be the event that Raymond sits beside one of the girls. Find P(A) and P(A').

26. A property investor is equally interested in buying properties P, Q, R, S, T, and U. He bought two of them at random.
    (a) List all his possible purchases.
    (b) Find the probability that
        (i)   property R is bought,
        (ii) properties R and Q are bought,
        (ii) property R is bought but not property Q.

27. In a game at a carnival, a card is first drawn at random from 3 cards that are numbered −9, 3, and 1. Another card is then drawn at random from 3 other cards that are numbered 2, −3, and 9.
    (a) List the sample space.
    (b) Find the probability that
        (i)   at most one of the numbers drawn is a positive number,
        (ii) at least one of the numbers drawn is a prime number.
    (c) The rule of the game states that a prize is won only if the sum of the numbers on the 2 drawn cards is positive. Is the rule fair to a player? Explain your answer.

28. 3 fair coins are tossed and their outcomes are noted.
    (a) List the sample space.
    (b) Find the probability of getting
        (i)   all heads,
        (ii) 2 heads and a tail,
        (iii) at most 1 head,
        (iv) no heads.

29. In the diagram, the diameters of the 3 circles are in the ratio 3 : 7 : 8.
    A point within the diagram is selected at random. Find the probability
    of selecting a point in
    (a) the smallest circle,
    (b) the shaded region,
    (c) the space between the biggest circle and the middle circle.

30. Let ξ be the set of employees in a company,

P = {employees in the company who earn more than \$2,000 a month}

and Q = {employees in the company who earn at least \$3,000 a month}.

(a) Describe the sets P' and Q'.

(b) Describe using '$\subset$', the relationship between

  (i) P and Q,

  (ii) P' and Q'.

31. The frequency table below shows the number of dogs owned by a group of children.

Number of dogs	0	1	2	3	4	5
Number of children	7	10	5	5	x	1

(a) The mean number of dogs owned by each child is 1.6. Form an equation in x and solve it.

(b) Hence, find the number of children in the group.

(c) A child is randomly selected. Find the probability of selecting a child with more than 3 dogs.

(d) A dog is randomly selected. Find the probability of selecting a dog that belongs to a child who has at most 3 dogs.

32. A box contains 200 buttons that are either blue or green. A button is randomly selected from the box.

(a) Find the number of each type of button if the probability of selecting a blue button is $\frac{11}{25}$.

(b) How many blue buttons must be removed from the 200 buttons so that the probability of selecting a green button will become $\frac{8}{13}$?

(c) How many blue buttons must be added to the 200 buttons so that the probability of selecting a green button will become $\frac{14}{27}$?

(d) When x blue buttons are added and x green buttons are removed from the 200 buttons, the probability of selecting either a blue or green button is the same. Find the value of x.

33. Jeffrey bought a grey (G), a red (R), a blue (B), and a yellow (Y) T-shirt. He also bought a blue (B), a white (W), and a grey (G) pair of jeans. Suppose that Jeffrey randomly matches a shirt with a pair of jeans.

(a) List all the possible ways of matching a shirt with a pair of jeans.

(b) Find the probability of Jeffrey wearing

  (i) a yellow T-shirt,

  (ii) a white pair of jeans.

(c) Let M be the event that Jeffrey matches a shirt with a pair of jeans of the same color. Find P(M) and P(M').

34. *ABCDE* is a 5-sided plane figure with sides of equal lengths.
$m\angle ABC = m\angle BCD = m\angle CDE = m\angle DEA = m\angle EAB = 108°$.

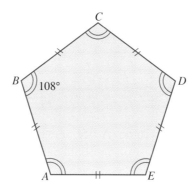

A triangle is drawn at random using three of the points *A*, *B*, *C*, *D*, and *E* as vertices.
(a) List the sample space.
(b) Let *X* be the event that *A* is a vertex of the drawn triangle. Find P(*X*) and P(*X*′).
(c) Let *Y* be the event that all the angles of the drawn triangle are acute angles.
    (i) Express *Y* using the listing method.
    (ii) Find P(*Y*).

Enrichment

---

35. Let *A* = {apple}, *B* = {banana, mango}, *C* = {cherry, mango, pear}.
  (a) List all the possible subsets of
    (i) *A*,   **(ii)** *B*,
    (iii) *C*.
  (b) If a set *P* has *n* elements, state the number of possible subsets of *P*.
  (c) Suggest a universal set ξ for the sets *A*, *B*, and *C*.

36. A telemarketing salesperson selects telephone numbers randomly from a telephone directory.
  (a) If one number is selected, what is the probability that the last two digits of the number are the same?
  (b) If 3 numbers are selected, what is the probability that the last digits of the 3 numbers are the same?
  (c) If 11 numbers are selected, what is the probability that at least two numbers have the same last digit?

37. In a digital clock, a digit is displayed using a 7-segment LCD unit. The diagrams below show the display for the digits 0 and 9.

  (a) Construct the display for the digits 1 to 8.
  (b) If the LCD unit displays a digit at random, what is the probability that it consists of the middle horizontal line segment?
  (c) Two LCD units are used to display the time in minutes, from 00 to 59. Find the probability that a random display has at least one digit
    (i) 3,   **(ii)** 8.

38.

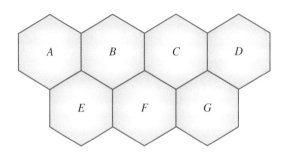

The diagram shows 7 cells in a honeycomb. A bee crawls from cell A to cell G. It always moves to an adjacent cell at random, either in the east or the south east direction.

(a) List the possible routes of the bee.

(b) Find the probability that the bee will pass through cell F.

39. An ecologist wanted to estimate the number of fish in a lake. He conducted an experiment of tag-and-recapture as follows:

> 1. In one day, he caught 100 fish from the lake and tagged each of them with a plastic label. The fish were then released into the lake.
> 2. On the next day, he caught 300 fish from the lake and counted the number of tagged ones among them.

(a) Suppose that the number of tagged fish caught on the next day was 20. Estimate the number of fish in the lake.

(b) Describe some assumptions that are required in using this estimation method.

17 Probability Of Combined Events

Basic Practice

1. A chip is drawn at random from 10 blue chips, 15 white chips, and 5 red chips. Find the probability that the chip drawn is
   (a) blue,
   (b) white or red,
   (c) not white,
   (d) green.

2. (a) List the sample space when a fair die is rolled.
   (b) Find the probability that
      (i) an even number is shown,
      (ii) a prime number is shown,
      (iii) an even or prime number is shown,
      (iv) a prime number which is even is shown,
      (v) a prime number which is not even is shown.

3. Twenty-five cards are numbered 11 to 35. A card is drawn at random. Find the probability that the number on the card is
   (a) at most 20,
   (b) at least 30,
   (c) a multiple of 5,
   (d) a factor of 100,
   (e) a multiple of 5 but not a factor of 100.

4. Two keys that are engraved with the letters F and G belong to two of the four locks that are painted blue and red respectively. The other two locks are painted white and yellow. A key and a lock are randomly selected.
   (a) Represent the sample space using a possibility diagram.
   (b) Hence, find the probability that
      (i) the selected key is engraved with the letter F and the selected lock is red,
      (ii) the selected key can unlock the selected lock,
      (iii) the selected key cannot unlock the selected lock.

5. Two fair dice, one red and one blue, are rolled.
   (a) Represent the sample space using a possibility diagram.
   (b) Hence, find the probability that the number shown on the red die is
      (i) equal to the number shown on the blue die,
      (ii) greater than the number shown on the blue die,
      (iii) at most equal to the number shown on the blue die,
      (iv) twice the number shown on the blue die.

6. A bag contains an equal number of yellow marbles, blue marbles, and red marbles. Two marbles are selected at random from the bag one at a time with replacement.
   (a) Represent the sample space using a tree diagram.
   (b) Hence, find the probability of selecting
       (i)   a yellow marble first followed by a blue marble,
       (ii)   a yellow marble and a blue marble,
       (iii) two marbles of the same color,
       (iv)   two marbles of different colors,
       (v)   two marbles which are not yellow.

7. Five cards are numbered 1 to 5. Two cards are drawn at random one at a time with replacement.
   (a) Draw a tree diagram, showing at each branch the two events: 'drawing a 3' and 'others'.
   (b) Hence, calculate the probability of drawing
       (i)   two 3's,
       (ii)   no 3's,
       (iii) a 3 followed by a card which is not numbered 3,
       (iv)   exactly one 3,
       (v)   at least one 3,
       (vi)   at most one 3.

8. A jar contains 4 lemon cookies and 6 strawberry cookies. Two cookies are selected at random from the jar, one by one, without replacement.
   (a) Represent the sample space using a tree diagram.
   (b) Hence, calculate the probability of selecting
       (i)   two cookies of the same flavor,
       (ii)   two cookies of different flavors,
       (iii) a lemon cookie on the second selection,
       (iv)   a strawberry cookie on the second selection.

9. The masses of 16 bars of the same dimensions are recorded below.

Mass (x g)	Number of bars
$80 \leqslant x < 90$	3
$90 \leqslant x < 100$	4
$100 \leqslant x < 110$	5
$110 \leqslant x < 120$	4

Two bars are randomly selected, one by one, without replacement. Find the probability of selecting
(a) two bars that each weighs less than 90 g,
(b) two bars that each weighs at least 100 g,
(c) a bar that weighs less than 90 g and a bar that weighs at least 100 g.

10. In a two-match tennis competition between team Alpha and team Beta, the probability of team Alpha winning a match is $\frac{1}{4}$. The probability of team Alpha losing a match is $\frac{1}{5}$. Calculate the probability of team Alpha

(a) neither winning nor losing the two matches,

(b) winning only one of the two matches,

(c) winning only the second match,

(d) winning the second match,

(e) winning the competition.

(**Further Practice**)

11. Suppose that the 13 spades from a pack of 52 playing cards are removed. Three cards are then drawn at random from the remaining 39 cards, one at a time with replacement. Calculate the probability of drawing

(a) 3 kings,
                                  (b) 3 red cards,

(c) 3 diamonds,
                          (d) a black card on the second draw,

(e) a jack, a queen, and a king.

12. The first 3 questions of a short quiz are true/false type and the 4th question is a multiple-choice type that has 4 possible answers. Suppose that random guesses are made when answering the 4 questions. Calculate the probability of

(a) answering all the questions correctly,

(b) answering all the questions incorrectly,

(c) answering the first 3 questions incorrectly but the 4th question correctly,

(d) answering at least 1 of the first 3 questions and the 4th question correctly.

13. A 52-page picture book contains objects that are arranged in alphabetical order. For example, pictures of objects that are spelled with an "A" are illustrated on page 1 and the corresponding spellings are shown on page 2, which is the facing page. Suppose that a toddler opens the book at random. Calculate the probability of the toddler opening

(a) pages 5 to 6,

(b) any page between page 5 and page 40,

(c) any page that illustrates and spells the letters "C" or "G",

(d) any page that illustrates and spells all the letters from "C" through "G",

(e) any page that illustrates and spells all the consonants.

(Note: In practice, books usually open with an odd page on the right.)

14. (a) One letter is randomly selected from the word *"HIPPOPOTAMUS"*. Calculate the probability that

    (i) a vowel is selected,

    (ii) either a "P" or a vowel is selected,

    (iii) neither a "P" nor a vowel is selected.

(b) If instead 3 letters are randomly selected one at a time without replacement.

    (i) Draw a tree diagram, showing at each branch the two events: 'P drawn' and 'others'.

    (ii) Hence, calculate the probability that

        (a) a "P" is first selected on the third draw,

        (b) three "P"s are selected,

        (c) none of the "P"s is selected,

        (d) at least one "P" is selected.

15. The face of a circular disk is divided into sectors A, B, C, and D as shown in the figure below.

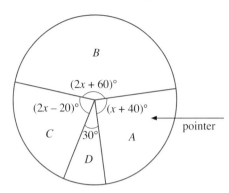

(a) Find the value of x.

(b) Which sector is the pointer least likely to indicate each time the disk is spun? Explain your answer.

(c) The disk is spun twice and the sector that the pointer indicates is noted after each spin. Calculate the probability that the pointer
   (i) will indicate the same sector each time,
   (ii) will indicate a different sector each time.

(d) Calculate the probability that the pointer will indicate the sector stated in (b) in at least one of 2 spins.

16. A batch of 10 components will be rejected upon first detecting a faulty component in a random test of 3 components, one after another without replacement. Suppose that there are 4 faulty components in a particular batch.

(a) Draw a tree diagram to represent the testing process, showing at each branch the two events: 'faulty' and 'good'.

(b) Hence, calculate the probability of
   (i) rejecting the batch after testing one component,
   (ii) rejecting the batch after testing two components,
   (iii) not rejecting the batch.

17. Shares of a particular company are offered for subscription in a manner listed below.

No. of Units Subscribed	No. of Units Available for Subscription	Chance of Success	No. of Units Allocated if Successful
1	1,000	$\frac{1}{10}$	1
5	1,000	$\frac{1}{6}$	2
10	1,000	$\frac{1}{3}$	3

Robert, Anthony, and William subscribed for 1, 5, and 10 units of shares respectively.

(a) Is the outcome of each of their subscription independent of one another? Explain your answer.

(b) Calculate the probability that
   (i) all of them are successful in their subscriptions,
   (ii) only one of them is successful,
   (iii) all of them are allocated a total of 3 units.

18. Suppose that 45% and 40% of residents approve and disapprove of the ideas of building a new highway near their neighborhood. If three residents are interviewed at random, find the probability that
   (a) all of them will either approve or disapprove of the idea,
   (b) at least two of them will not approve of the idea,
   (c) at most one of them will approve of the idea.

Challenging Practice

19. Five army recruits were reporting back to their barrack on the same bus. As they were late, the recruits gave the excuse that the bus they were on had a punctured tire. To verify if the recruits are telling the truth, the duty officer separated the recruits and questioned them one by one on the position of the punctured tire.

If each recruit randomly selects a tire, calculate the probability of
   (a) exposing their excuse upon questioning the second recruit,
   (b) exposing their excuse upon questioning the fifth recruit,
   (c) not exposing their excuse upon questioning all the recruits.

20. A shopper was given the chance to draw a prize, which may be a $10 shopping voucher or a $100 shopping voucher. Bin A, which has 90 $10 vouchers, 10 $100 vouchers and bin B which initially has 20 $10 vouchers and 4 $100 vouchers are used for the draw.

A voucher is first randomly selected from bin A. The selected voucher is then placed in bin B and a voucher is then selected from bin B. The shopper will take away the selected voucher from bin B as the prize.
   (a) Represent the sample space using a tree diagram.
   (b) Calculate the probability of selecting a $100 voucher from bin A.
   (c) Calculate the probability of the shopper winning a
       (i) $10 voucher,
       (ii) $100 voucher.

21. $WXYZ$ is a flat square base of an open cubical container. The points A, B, C, and D are on the perimeter of $WXYZ$ and are such that $WA : AX = WD : DZ = YC : CZ = 3 : 2$ and $XB : BY = 1 : 4$. The point O is the center of $WXYZ$.
   (a) A game is played whereby a player tosses a marble into the container. The position of the marble is noted when it finally comes to rest. Find the probability that the marble will rest inside the shaded regions.
   (b) Suppose that the marble is tossed twice into the container and removed each time after its final position is noted.

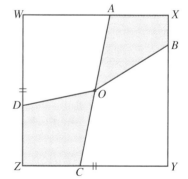

If the marble is outside the shaded regions each time, the player wins $1. Otherwise, the player loses $1. Is this a fair game? Explain your answer.

22. A bag contains 6 green balls and 2 red balls. One ball is drawn from the bag at random and its color is observed. The ball and 2 additional balls of the observed color are placed into the bag. Find the probability that the next ball drawn will be red.

23. John and Linda compete in a chess match of up to 3 games. The match ends when one of them wins two games. In each game, the probability that John will win is 45%. Find the probability that John will win the match.

(**Enrichment**)

---

24. A dart board is in the shape of an equilateral $\triangle ABC$ of side 20 cm. M, N, and P are the midpoints of the sides of $\triangle ABC$. Five darts are thrown at random on the board. Find the probability that
   (a) all darts land on $\triangle MNP$,
   (b) at least one dart lands on $\triangle MNP$,
   (c) exactly one dart lands on $\triangle MNP$,
   (d) there are at least two darts whose distance apart is at most 10 cm.

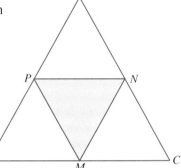

25. The following table shows the distribution of probability in throwing a die, where k is a constant.

Score	1	2	3	4	5	6
Probability	k	0.05	0.18	0.17	0.04	k^2

   (a) Find the value of k.
   (b) If the die is thrown twice, find the probability that
      (i) the scores are the same,
      (ii) the product of the scores is even.

26. The diagram shows a target of darts. It consists of 3 regions bounded by concentric circles of radii r cm, $2r$ cm, and $3r$ cm. Suppose that a dart always lands on the target at random and the numbers on the target indicate the scores obtained for landing on those regions.
   (a) If a dart is thrown on the target, find the probability of getting
      (i) 1 point,
      (ii) 3 points,
      (iii) 5 points.
   (b) Suppose two darts are thrown,
      (i) what are the possible scores?
      (ii) what are the probabilities of those scores in **(b)(i)**?

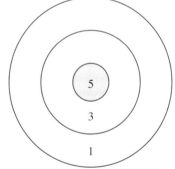

27. A computer system can complete a task if at least $\frac{1}{2}$ of its central processing units (CPU) are working. The probability that a CPU will fail is 0.005. The failures of all CPUs are independent of each other. Find the probability that the task can be completed if the system has
   (a) 2 CPUs,
   (b) 3 CPUs.
   Give your answers correct to 6 decimal places.

Answers

Chapter 9　Number Patterns
Basic Practice

1. (a) 16, 19   (b) 39, 47   (c) 61, 73
    (d) 77, 90   (e) 11, 7   (f) 1, –8
    (g) –5, –12   (h) –8, –24

2. (a) 81, 243   (b) 128, 512   (c) 40.5, 60.75
    (d) 8, 4   (e) 96, –192   (f) –512, 2,048
    (g) 100, –50   (h) –5, 1

3. (a) 20, 26   (b) 33, 45   (c) 41, 54
    (d) 8, 10   (e) 720, 5,040   (f) $\frac{9}{10}, \frac{11}{12}$
    (g) $\frac{14}{33}, \frac{17}{40}$ (h) $\frac{55}{89}, \frac{144}{233}$

4. (a) 8, 11, 14   (b) 5, 1, –3
    (c) –13, –18, –23   (d) $8\frac{1}{2}, 8, 7\frac{1}{2}$
    (e) 81, 121, 169   (f) 30, 88, 156
    (g) 0, 12, 60   (h) $\frac{1}{3}, \frac{4}{5}, 1$

5. (a) 59   (b) –8   (c) –1,160
    (d) 3,192   (e) 2   (f) $4\frac{1}{2}$

6. (a) 28, 48, 68   (b) 88   (c) 108

7. (a) 25, 18, 11
    (b) –38
    (c) (i) 4   (ii) –3

8. (a) 143, 567   (b) 710

9. (a) 9   (b) 14

10. (a) 3   (b) 8

Further Practice

11. (a) 31, 35   (b) 50, 57
    (c) –7, –13   (d) –4, –13
    (e) 8,192, –32,768   (f) 364.5, 546.75
    (g) 64, $42\frac{2}{3}$ (h) –6, 3

12. (a) 9, 12, 15, 18
    (b) 36
    (c) No, 41 is not a multiple of 3.

13. (a) $-1, \frac{1}{2}, 3, 6\frac{1}{2}$ (b) $48\frac{1}{2}$

14. (a) $T_n = 3n + 1$ (b) $T_n = 7n - 2$
    (c) $T_n = 9n - 17$ (d) $T_n = -4n + 11$
    (e) $T_n = -11n + 45$ (f) $T_n = -8n + 53$

15. (a) $T_n = 4n^2$ (b) 256
    (c) Yes, because the square root of 4 is 2 and the square root of n^2 is n.

16. (a) 3, 5, 7, 9
    (b) (i) 33   (ii) 57   (iii) 123
    (c) $2n + 1$

17. (a) $T_n = -6n + 44$
    (b) (i) $T_n = -6n + 47$ (ii) $T_n = -6n + 40$
    (iii) $T_n = -3n + 22$

18. (a) 39, 43   (b) 51, 55, 59

19. (a)

n	1	2	3	4
T_n	3	7	11	15
P_n	18	30	42	54

    (b) (i) $T_n = 4n - 1$ (ii) 27, 31
    (c) (i) $P_n = 12n + 6$ (ii) 90, 102

20. (a) $D_1 = 5, D_2 = 8, D_3 = 11, D_4 = 14$
    (b) $D_n = 3S_n + 2$
    (c) (i) 47   (ii) 20

Challenging Practice

21. (a) $\frac{31}{32}, \frac{63}{64}$ (b) $T_n = \frac{2^n - 1}{2^n}$ (c) 1

22. (a)

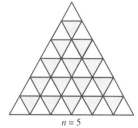

$n = 5$

    (b) (i) $S_1 = 1, S_2 = 3, S_3 = 6, S_4 = 10$
    (ii) $U_1 = 3, U_2 = 6, U_3 = 10, U_4 = 15$
    (iii) $S_1 + U_1 = 4, S_2 + U_2 = 9, S_3 + U_3 = 16,$
        $S_4 + U_4 = 25$
    (c) (i) $S_n + U_n = (n + 1)^2$ (ii) 256

23. (a)

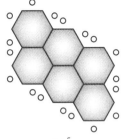

$n = 5$

(b)

n	1	2	3	4
H_n	2	3	4	5
C_n	10	12	14	16

(c) **(i)** $H_n = n + 1$ **(ii)** $C_n = 2n + 8$

(d) **(i)** 26 **(ii)** 22

(e) No. p is a positive integer.
∴ $2p$ is even and $2p + 1$ is odd.
But all the figures have an even number of circles.
∴ there will be no figures with $(2p + 1)$ circles.

24. (a)

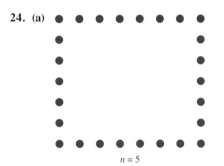

$n = 5$

(b) **(i)** $D_1 = 10, D_2 = 14, D_3 = 18, D_4 = 22$
(ii) $A_1 = 24, A_2 = 48, A_3 = 80, A_4 = 120$

(c) **(i)** $D_n = 4n + 6$
(ii) 54

(d) **(i)** $A_n = (2n + 4)(2n + 2)$
(ii) 728 cm^2

(e) **(i)** 14
(ii) 960 cm^2

25. (a) **(i)** $x + 1, x + 5, x + 6$
(ii) $4x + 12$

(c) 25

Enrichment

26. (a) **(i)** $\frac{1}{3}$ **(ii)** $\frac{2}{5}$

(iii) $\frac{3}{7}$ **(iv)** $\frac{4}{9}$

(b) **(i)** $\frac{9}{19}$ **(ii)** $\frac{n}{2n + 1}$

27. (a) 5th term $= 4x + 9y$
6th term $= 3x + 11y$

(b) $(9 - n)x + (2n - 1)y$

(c) 12

28. (a)

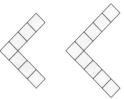

$n = 4$ $n = 5$

(b)

n	1	2	3	4	5
M_n	1	3	5	7	9
P_n	20	40	60	80	100

(c) $M_n = 2n - 1$
(d) $P_n = 20n$

29. (a)

$n = 5$ $n = 6$

(b) 5th pentagonal number = 35
6th pentagonal number = 51

(c) $a_n = \frac{1}{2}n(3n - 1)$

Chapter 10   Coordinates And Linear Graphs

Basic Practice

1. (a) $A(3, 1)$, $B(-3, 1)$, $C(-2, -1)$, $D(1, -2)$, $E(4, 3)$,
$F(-4, 4)$, $G(-2, -3)$, $H(3, -4)$, $I(2, 0)$, $J(0, -3)$

(b) A, D, E, H, I

(c) C, D, G, H, J

2. (b) B and J
(c) D and H

3. (b) **(ii)** Right-angled triangle
(c) 21 unit^2

4. (a)

x	-2	-1	0	1	2
$y = 2x + 1$	-3	-1	1	3	5

(c) $\left(-\frac{1}{2}, 0\right)$

(d) 2

(e) $1\frac{1}{2}$

5. (a)

x	-2	0	2	4	6
$y = -x + 5$	7	5	3	1	-1

(c) No
(d) **(ii)** $(-1, 6)$

6. (b) $(6, 0)$ **(c)** Yes

7. **(b)** **(i)** $(6, 0)$ **(ii)** $(0, 3)$
     (c) $(2, 2)$

8. **(b)** **(i)** $(-2, 5)$, $(-2, -1)$, $(4, 5)$, and $(4, -1)$
     (ii) Square

9. Slope of $L_1 = -\dfrac{1}{2}$

    Slope of $L_2 = 1\dfrac{2}{3}$

    Slope of $L_3 = 1$

    Slope of $L_4 = -1\dfrac{1}{2}$

    Slope of $L_5 = 0$

10. Slope of $L_1 = -\dfrac{3}{4}$

     Slope of $L_2 = 1$

     Slope of $L_3 = -1\dfrac{1}{2}$

     Slope of $L_4 = 4\dfrac{1}{2}$

Further Practice

11. **(b)** Trapezoid
     (c) **(ii)** $(-1, -2)$

12. **(b)** Scalene triangle   **(c)** $(3, -1)$
     (d) $(2, -1)$

13. **(b)** **(i)** 3rd quadrant   **(ii)** 4th quadrant
     (c) $(-1, 1)$
     (d) $(1, 1)$

14. **(b)** **(i)** $\left(-1\dfrac{1}{2}, 8\right)$ **(ii)** 2nd quadrant

     (c) **(i)** $\left(4\dfrac{1}{2}, -4\right)$ **(ii)** 4th quadrant

15. **(b)** **(i)** $p = 0$, $q = 1\dfrac{1}{2}$
     (ii) The points A and B have the same coordinates.
     (c) $(3, 6)$

16. **(b)** **(ii)** $x = -1$, $x = 2$, $y = 1$, $y = -1$
     (c) **(i)** $(-1, 1)$, $(2, 1)$, $(2, -1)$, and $(-1, -1)$
     (ii) $1 : 3$

17. **(a)** 12 **(b)** $\dfrac{1}{3}$ **(c)** 4

18. **(b)** $D(-1, 0)$
     (c) Slope of $AB = -\dfrac{1}{3}$

        Slope of $BC = \dfrac{1}{3}$

        Slope of $CD = -\dfrac{1}{3}$

        Slope of $AD = \dfrac{1}{3}$

     (d) The slopes of the opposite sides of a rhombus are equal.

19. **(a)** AB is a horizontal line.
        AC is a vertical line.
     (b) **(i)** 2 **(ii)** $(1, -2)$
     (c) $(-1, 2)$
     (d) -2

20. **(b)** **(i)** 2 **(ii)** 2
     (c) The points A, B, and C lie on the same straight line.

Challenging Practice

21. **(a)** $(3, 1)$ or $(6, 2)$
     (b) $(5, 1)$ or $(6, 2)$
     (c) $(2, 2)$, $(3, 2)$, $(5, 2)$, $(2, 3)$, $(3, 3)$, or $(5, 3)$
     (d) $(3, 1)$ or $(6, 1)$

22. **(a)** **(ii)** $-\dfrac{1}{2}$ **(b)** $(-3, 2)$ **(c)** $(1, 0)$

23. **(b)** Slope $= \dfrac{4}{5}$ or 0.8
        For every mile traveled, 80¢ is charged.
     (c) $\dfrac{5}{2}$, i.e., 2.5 means the flag-down charge is $2.50.
     (d) **(i)** $8.50
     (ii) 2.5 mile

24. **(b)** Slope $= 2$
        The goat gained 2 kg every month.
     (c) 30 kg
     (d) **(i)** 3 kg
     (ii) $2\dfrac{1}{2}$ months

25. **(b)** The father is moving faster.
        The slope of $y_2 = 2t$ is greater than the slope of $y_1 = t + 20$.
     (c) 5 m
     (d) $p = 20$ and $q = 40$

Enrichment

26. **(a)** $B(8, 5)$, $C(3, 8)$ **(b)** 34 unit^2

27. **(a)** '$(4, 5)$, $(5, 5)$, $(1, 5)$, $(6, 3)$'
     (b) '$PILLOW$'
     (c) $\dfrac{1}{3}$

28. **(b)** The points lie on a staight line.
     (c) $y = -\dfrac{1}{2}x + 1$

29. **(a)**

x	0	20	40	60	80
y	-100	-20	60	140	220

     (c) Profit $= -$100$ or Loss $= 100
     (d) 25
     (e) 50
     (f) 4. The slope means that the additional profit for every additional T-shirt sold is $4.

Chapter 11   Inequalities

Basic Practice

1. (a) Yes   (b) No   (c) No   (d) Yes
   (e) Yes   (f) Yes   (g) No   (h) Yes
   (i) No   (j) Yes

2. (a) $x > 6$ (b) $x > 8$ (c) $x < -6$
   (d) $x < 4.5$ (e) $x \geq 4.5$ (f) $x \geq -3.75$
   (g) $x \leq 2.25$ (h) $x \leq -2\frac{2}{3}$

3. (a) 2, 4, 6, 8, 10, 12, 14, 16, 18, 20
   (b) (i) $x = 2, 4, 6,$ or 8 (ii) $x = 14, 16, 18, 20$
   (iii) $x = 2, 4, 6, 8$ (iv) $x = 14, 16, 18, 20$
   (v) $x = 2$ (vi) $x = 18, 20$
   (vii) $x = 2, 4$ (viii) $x = 18, 20$

4. (a) 2, 3, 5, 7, 11, 13, 17, 19, 23, 29
   (b) (i) $x = 2, 3, 5, 7, 11, 13$
   (ii) $x = 29$
   (iii) $x = 2, 3, 5, 7, 11, 13, 17$
   (iv) $x = 23, 29$
   (v) $x = 2, 3, 5$
   (vi) $x = 11, 13, 17, 19, 23, 29$
   (vii) $x = 2, 3$
   (viii) $x = 17, 19, 23, 29$

5. (a) $-5, -3, -1, 1, 3, 5$
   (b) (i) $x = -5, -3$ (ii) $x = 5$
   (iii) $x = -5, -3$ (iv) $x = 5$
   (v) $x = -3, -5$ (vi) $x = -1, 1, 3, 5$
   (vii) $x = -5$ (viii) $x = 5$

6. (a) 10   (b) 11   (c) 11
   (d) 16   (e) 27

7. (a) $>$ (b) $\leq$ (c) $>$
   (d) $\leq$ (e) $>$ (f) $\geq$
   (g) $>$ (h) $<$

8. (a) $x > 7$ (b) $x < 15$ (c) $x \geq 2$
   (d) $x > -7$ (e) $x \leq -3$ (f) $x < 4$
   (g) $x \geq 4$ (h) $x > -4$

9. (a) (i) 12   (ii) -2
   (iii) -1 (iv) -1
   (b) (i) 3   (ii) 6
   (iii) -9 (iv) 4

10. (a) $\$2x$ (b) 1, 2, 3, 4, or 5

11. (a) $\frac{x}{120}$
    (b) The volume of the tank is more than 1,800 cm^3.

12. (a) $\frac{1}{2}x$ km
    (b) Joyce's average speed is more than 6.4 km/h.

13. (a) $65x$¢
    (b) (i) 8   (ii) \$0.30

Further Practice

14. (a) $x > 15$ (b) $x < -20$ (c) $x \geq -12$
    (d) $x \leq 15$ (e) $x > -15$ (f) $x < -6$
    (g) $x \geq 9$ (h) $x \leq 1.5$

15. (a) $x > 7$ (b) $x < -6$ (c) $x \geq 1\frac{1}{2}$
    (d) $x \leq -4$ (e) $x > 18$ (f) $x < -4$
    (g) $x \geq 70$ (h) $x \leq -8$

16. (a) $x = 10$ (b) $x = -9$ (c) $x = 18$
    (d) $x = -5$ (e) $x = 8$ (f) $x = -6$
    (g) $x = 15$ (h) $x = -9$

17. (a) $x = 6$ (b) $x = -9$ (c) $x = 15$
    (d) $x = -10$ (e) $x = 3$ (f) $x = -9$
    (g) $x = 0$ (h) $x = -5$

18. (a) $x > 40$
    (b) (i) 42   (ii) 41   (iii) 48

19. (a) $x < 15$
    (b) (i) $x = 3, 6, 9, 12$
    (ii) $x = 1, 2, 3, 4, 5, 6, 10, 12$

20. (a) $x > 7\frac{3}{8}$ (b) $x \geq 61$ (c) $x \leq 3\frac{2}{7}$
    (d) $x > 1\frac{13}{31}$ (e) $x \geq -\frac{3}{4}$ (f) $x < 1\frac{41}{58}$
    (g) $x > 1\frac{7}{13}$ (h) $x \leq -\frac{256}{271}$

21. (a) $T_n = 12n$ (b) 108   (c) 192

22. (a) $15x$ cm^2
    (b) (i) $15x \geq 70$ (ii) $x \geq 4\frac{2}{3}$
    (c) 75 cm^2

23. (a) $x \leq 4.2$ (b) 80 cm

24. (a) $\frac{x}{30}\%$
    (b) (i) $x < 150$ (ii) \$3,149

25. (a) At least 24 points   (b) At least 45 points

26. (a) $6 + 0.55x \leq 13$ (b) $x \leq 12\frac{8}{11}$
    (c) 12   (d) \$0.40

27. (a) $\dfrac{20(x + 1) + 30(2x - 5)}{50} < 4$
    (b) $x < 4\frac{1}{8}$

28. (a) (i) 8   (ii) 56 cm
    (b) (i) $x \leqslant 9$ (ii) $y \leqslant 42$

Challenging Practice

29. (a) (i) $x > 24$ (ii) $y < 36$
    (b) (i) 25   (ii) 35
      (iii) 15   (iv) 1.4
    (c) 4

30. (a) $\$4.3x$
    (b) $x \leqslant 4\frac{8}{43}$
    (c) 8 cherry pies, 12 apple pies
    (d) $\$0.80$

31 (b) (i) $p > 5$ (ii) $q < 3$
    (c) (i) $(2, 7)$ (ii) Quadrant I

32. (a) $\$(47x - 5)$
    (b) $x > 4\frac{22}{47}$
    (c) (i) $x \geqslant 8$ (ii) 8
      (iii) $\$371$

33. (a) $1\frac{5}{6}x$ km   (b) $3\frac{1}{7}x$ km/hr
    (c) Not reasonable

34. (a) Star Transport: $\$(1.25 + 1.5x)$
      Regent Pte. Ltd.: $\$(2.8 + x)$
    (b) For distances less than 3.1 km

35. (a) 9 desks, 16 chairs
    (b) 6 desks, 27 chairs

36. (a) (i) 2 pens, 28 pencils
      (ii) $\$9.50$
    (b) (i) 6 pens, 20 pencils
      (ii) $\$9.30$

Enrichment

37. (a) $\$0 \leqslant$ price of the spoon $\leqslant \$1.80$
    (b) 25

38. (a) 360 to 540
    (b) 80 m^2 to $106\frac{2}{3}$ m^2

39. (a) (i) $\$144$
      (ii) $\$162$
    (b) $0\% <$ discount percentage $< 16\frac{2}{3}\%$

40. (a) 0 km < possible distance traveled < 10 km
    (b) $6\frac{2}{3}$ km/hr

41. 91 cm

42. 18, 19, or 20

43. (b) $\frac{45}{17}$ and $\frac{127}{48}$

Chapter 12   Perimeters And Areas Of Plane Figures

Basic Practice

1. (a) Area = 49 cm^2
      Perimeter = 28 cm
    (b) Area = x^2 cm^2
      Perimeter = $4x$ cm
    (c) Area $36x^2$ cm^2
      Perimeter = $24x$ cm

2. (a) Area = 40 cm^2
      Perimeter = 26 cm
    (b) Area = $(18x + 27)$ cm^2
      Perimeter = $(4x + 24)$ cm
    (c) Area = $(12x^2 - 15x)$ cm^2
      Perimeter = $(14x - 10)$ cm

3. (a) Area = 16π cm^2
      Circumference = 8π cm
    (b) Area = $25x^2\pi$ cm^2
      Circumference = $10x\pi$ cm
    (c) Area = 56.25π cm^2
      Circumference = 15π cm
    (d) Area = $9y^2\pi$ cm^2
      Circumference = $6y\pi$ cm

4. (a) 54 cm^2 (b) $12x$ cm^2
    (c) $(8y^2 + 6y)$ cm^2

5. (a) $3\frac{1}{2}$ (b) 8
    (c) 12   (d) 12

6. (a) 21 cm^2 (b) $(18x - 42)$ cm^2
    (c) $32x^2$ cm^2 (d) $(8x^2 + 12x)$ cm^2

7. (a) 30 cm^2 (b) 150 cm^2
    (c) $(10x^2 + 6x)$ cm^2 (d) $5x^2$ cm^2

8. (a) 18   (b) 3
    (c) 28   (d) 25

9. (a) Perimeter = 50 cm
      Area = 140 cm^2
    (b) Perimeter = 41.2 cm
      Area = 65 cm^2
    (c) Perimeter = 40π cm or 126 cm
      Area = $(400 + 200\pi)$ cm^2 or 1,030 cm^2
    (d) Perimeter = 40 cm
      Area = 76.8 cm^2

10. **(a)** Perimeter = 64 cm
Area = 132 cm^2
(b) Perimeter = 64.278 cm
Area = 69.498 cm^2
(c) Perimeter = 32 cm
Area = 30 cm^2
(d) Perimeter = 120 cm
Area = 468 cm^2

Further Practice

11. **(a)** **(i)** 9 cm   **(ii)** 36 cm
    (b) 12 cm

12. **(a)** **(i)** 114 cm   **(ii)** 800 cm^2
    (b) **(i)** 40 cm   **(ii)** 25%
    (c) 200%

13. **(a)** 288π cm^2 **(b)** 96π cm

14. **(b)** **(i)** 12.5 unit^2 **(ii)** 9 unit^2
    (c) **(i)** 10 unit^2 **(ii)** 6 unit^2

15. **(a)** Parallelogram
    (b) **(i)** 10 cm   **(ii)** 120 cm^2
       (iii) 480 cm^2
    (c) $27\frac{9}{13}$ cm or 27.7 cm

16. **(a)**

    (b) 56 cm
    (c) **(i)** $A_1 = 24$, $A_2 = 48$, $A_3 = 72$, $A_4 = 96$
       (ii) $A_n = 24n$
    (d) 360 cm^2

17. **(a)** 2 : 3   **(b)** 2 : 1
    (c) 1 : 2   **(d)** 11 : 6

18. **(a)** Trapezoid   **(b)** 40 cm
    (c) 83.16 cm^2 **(d)** 34.7 cm^2

19. **(a)** 225 cm^2 **(b)** 56.25%

20. **(a)** Length = 48 cm, Width = 32 cm
    (b) 768 cm^2
    (c) **(i)** $(1536 - 384\pi)$ cm^2 or 330 cm^2
       (ii) $(160 + 96\pi)$ cm or 462 cm

Challenging Practice

22. **(a)** **(i)** 13.8 m   **(ii)** 5.59 m^2
    (b) 10 km
    (c) **(i)** $x = 724.6$ **(ii)** 724

23. **(b)** 165 unit^2 **(c)** 272 unit^2

24. **(a)** $(14 + 2x)$ cm^2
    (c) $(59 + 11x)$ cm^2
    (d) **(i)** $x = 2$ **(ii)** 18 cm^2

25. **(a)** 218 cm   **(b)** 2,491 cm^2

Enrichment

26. 77 cm^2

27. **(a)** 289 cm^2 **(b)** 49 cm^2
    (c) 60 cm^2 **(d)** 529 cm^2

28. **(a)** 405 cm^2 **(b)** 10 cm

29. 45π cm^2

Chapter 13   Volumes And Surface Areas Of Solids

Basic Practice

1. **(a)** Volume = 64 cm^3
Total surface area = 96 cm^2
    (b) Volume = 421.875 cm^3
Total surface area = 337.5 cm^2
    (c) Volume = $\frac{1}{8}$ cm^3
Total surface area = 1.5 cm^2
    (d) Volume = $\frac{27}{64}$ cm^3
Total surface area = 3.375 cm^2
    (e) Volume = x^3 cm^3
Total surface area = $6x^2$ cm^2
    (f) Volume = $8x^3$ cm^3
Total surface area = $24x^2$ cm^2

2. **(a)** Volume = 120 cm^3
Total surface area = 148 cm^2
    (b) Volume = 108 cm^3
Total surface area = 147 cm^2
    (c) Volume = 189 cm^3
Total surface area = 223.5 cm^2
    (d) Volume = $21x$ cm^3
Total surface area = $(42 + 20x)$ cm^2
    (e) Volume = $(6x + 6)$ cm^3
Total surface area = $(10x + 22)$ cm^2
    (f) Volume = $2x^2$ cm^3
Total surface area = $(4x^2 + 6x)$ cm^2
    (g) Volume = xy cm^3
Total surface area = $(2xy + 2x + 2y)$ cm^2
    (h) Volume = $12xy$ cm^3
Total surface area = $(12xy + 8x + 12y)$ cm^2

3. (a) Volume = 4,096 cm^3
   Total surface area = 1,536 cm^2
   (b) (i) 8 cm (ii) 3,072 cm^2
   (c) 100%

4. (a) Volume = 300 cm^3
   Total surface area = 280 cm^2
   (b) Volume = 210 cm^3
   Total surface area = 270 cm^2
   (c) Volume = 266 cm^3
   Total surface area = 272 cm^2
   (d) Volume = 155 cm^3
   Total surface area = 192 cm^2

5. (a) 3,240 cm^3 (b) 1,332 cm^2

6. (a) Volume = 3,000 cm^3
   Total surface area = 1,490 cm^2
   (b) 1,730 cm^2
   (c) 16.1%

7. (a) 36 cm (b) 67,500 cm^3
   (c) 37.5%

8. (a) (i) 5 m^2 (ii) 745.6 m^2
   (iii) 0.832 m^2 (iv) 0.0063 m^2
   (b) (i) 60,000 cm^2 (ii) 94,000 cm^2
   (iii) 300 cm^2 (iv) 8,750 cm^2

9. (a) (i) 2 m^3 (ii) 0.345 m^3
   (iii) 0.0006 m^3 (iv) 0.000025 m^3
   (b) (i) 3,000,000 cm^3 (ii) 4,500,000 cm^3
   (iii) 100,000 cm^3 (iv) 250,000 cm^3

10. (a) 16 cm
    (b) (i) 54,000 cm^3 (ii) 0.054 m^3
    (c) (i) 7,215 cm^2 (ii) 0.7215 m^2

Further Practice

11. (a) 864 cm^2
    (b) (i) $x = 16$ (ii) 1,680 cm^3

12. (a) (i) 26 (ii) 364 cm^2
    (b) 13.65 cm
    (c) 4,968.6 cm^3

13. (a) 133 cm^3 (b) 166 cm^2

14. (a) Trapezoidal prism
    (b) (i) 96 cm (ii) 184 cm^2
    (iii) 144 cm^3

15. (b) 156 cm^2

16. (a) Volume = 700 cm^3
    Total surface area = 702 cm^2
    (b) Volume = 2,160 cm^3
    Total surface area = 1,376 cm^2

(c) Volume = 1,104 cm^3
   Total surface area = 708 cm^2
(d) Volume = 396 cm^3
   Total surface area = 426 cm^2

17. Volume = 280 cm^3
    Total surface area = 262 cm^2

18. (a) 180 cm^2 (b) $x = 5$
    (c) 1,772.5 cm^2

19. (a) 189 cm^3 (b) 225 cm^2
    (c) $160.65 (d) $22.50

20. (a) (i) 60,840 cm^3 (ii) $x = 65$
    (b) (i) 1,625 cm^3 (ii) 35
    (c) 60.76 cm

Challenging Practice

21. 459 m^3

22. (a) (i) 32 cm (ii) 8 : 9
    (b) (i) 1.6 cm (ii) 5,120 cm^3
    (iii) 3,840 cm^2

23. (a) (i) 37,500 cm^3 (ii) 0.0375 m^3
    (b) (i) 6 cm (ii) 8 cm
    (iii) 656 cm^2
    (c) $x = 6, y = 4.5$

24. (a) 6,500 m^3 (b) 3,000 m^3
    (c) 7 hr 55 min

25. (a) $V_2 = 7, V_3 = 10, A_1 = 18$
    (b) (i) $V_n = 3n + 1$ (ii) $A_n = 12n + 6$
    (d) (i) 25 cm^3 (ii) $p = 8$

Enrichment

26. (a) 1,625 cm^2 (b) 6.91 cm

27. (a) (i) 22 cm^2 (ii) 24 cm^2
    (iii) 26 cm^2

28. (a) 30 m^2
    (b) 15.75 m^3
    (c) (i) $10.5n$ m^2 (ii) $1.35(n + 1)$ m^3

Chapter 14 Proportions

Basic Practice

1. (a) 1 : 60 (b) 1 : 144
   (c) 1 : 1,056 (d) 1 : 55
   (e) 1 : 20,000 (f) 1 : 12,500
   (g) 1 : 40,000 (h) 1 : 20,000

2. **(a)** 2.5 km **(b)** 15 km
   (c) 2 km **(d)** 6.25 km
   (e) 7.5 km **(f)** 11.25 km

3. **(a)** 2 cm **(b)** 12 cm
   (c) 1.5 cm **(d)** 7 cm
   (e) 1.6 cm **(f)** 3.8 cm

4. **(a)** 0.16 km^2 **(b)** 2.4 km^2
   (c) 0.096 km^2 **(d)** 1.52 km^2
   (e) 0.8 km^2 **(f)** 12.8 km^2

5. **(a)** 25 cm^2 **(b)** 100 cm^2
   (c) 17.5 cm^2 **(d)** 140 cm^2
   (e) 1.5 cm^2 **(f)** 37.5 cm^2

6. **(a)** $y = 6x$
   (b) (i) 72 **(ii)** 7

7. **(a)** $V = \frac{1}{2}r^3$
   (b) (i) 62.5 **(ii)** 6

8. **(a)** $pq = 96$
   (b) (i) 32 **(ii)** 12

9. **(a)** $b^2C = 10$
   (b) (i) 0.4 **(ii)** 10

10. **(a)** 2 **(b)** 10
    (c) 64

Further Practice

11. **(a)** $\frac{1}{25,000}$
    (b) (i) 6.75 km **(ii)** 2.75 km^2

12. **(a)** 1 : 25,000 **(b)** 2.375 km
    (c) 600 mm

13. **(a) (i)** 1 : 50,000 **(ii)** 1 : 40,000
    (b) 20 cm

14. **(a)** $\frac{4}{3}$
    (b) (i) 3,750 **(ii)** 600 m
    (c) (i) 1.125 cm^2 **(ii)** 2 cm^2

15. **(a) (i)** $m = 3V$ **(ii)** $V = 4\frac{4}{21}r^3$
    (iii) $m = 12\frac{4}{7}r^3$
    (b) (i) $100\frac{4}{7}$ g **(ii)** $3\frac{1}{2}$ cm

16. **(c) (i)** $y - 2 = 3x$ **(ii)** $y = 3x + 2$

17. **(c) (i)** $(x - 1)y = 100$ or $y = \frac{100}{x-1}$
    (ii) 21

18. **(a)** $y = 14\sqrt{x}$ **(b)** 112
    (c) 49

19. **(a)** $xy = 80$ **(b)** 1.6
    (c) 64

20. **(a)** $p = \frac{100}{q^2}$ **(b)** 4

Challenging Practice

21. **(a)** 1 : 8
    (b) (i) 400,000 **(ii)** 2.5 km^2
    (c) (i) 2 km **(ii)** 2 cm

22. 5 : 8

23. **(a)** 2 **(b)** 45.5

24. **(a) (i)** 20 **(ii)** 45
    (iii) 1.25
    (b) (i) 300% **(ii)** 800%
    (iii) −75%

25. **(a) (i)** 67.5 **(ii)** 20
    (iii) 4,320
    (b) (i) −87.5% **(ii)** −96.3%
    (iii) 700%

Enrichment

26. **(a)** $312.50 **(b)** the ball of radius 4 cm

27. **(a) (i)** 1,200 units **(ii)** 600 units
    (b) 4,800 units

28. **(b)** 8,100 cm^2

29. **(a)** length = 10 cm, area = 16 cm^2
    (b) 1 : 1.25r

Chapter 15   Data Handling

Basic Practice

1. **(a)** taking measurements
   (b) 1, 2, 3, 4, 5, or 6

2. **(a)** 15 **(b)** 10

3. **(a)** 26 **(b)** 10 **(c)** 24

4. **(a) (i)** 10 **(ii)** 12
   (iii) 6 **(iv)** 0
   (v) −5 **(vi)** 4x
   (vii) 3y **(viii)** 8
   (b) (i) 6.4 **(ii)** $6\frac{2}{3}$
   (iii) 2.4

5. (a) (i) 4.5 cm   **(ii)** 5.75 cm
  (b) boys
  (c) girls

6. (a) 23   **(b)** 36
  (c) 29   **(d)** 51.5
  (e) 67   **(f)** 71.5
  (g) $w - 1$ **(h)** $3w + 4$

7. (a) 201   **(b)** $203\frac{11}{16}$ km/hr

8. (a) 7   **(b)** 74
  (c) 58 and 101   **(d)** No mode
  (e) $2w$ **(f)** $w + 4$

9. (a) mean = $2\frac{2}{3}$ **(b)** mean = 3
     median = 2   median = 3
     mode = 2   mode = 2
  (c) mean = −0.575, median = −1, mode = −2

10. (a) 24   **(b)** 4.5
  (c) 24   **(c)** 18

Further Practice

11. (a) reading publications
  (b) observing outcomes
  (c) conducting surveys

12. (a) 20   **(b)** 2
  (c) 3

13. (a) 4   **(b)** 25%
  (c) 77

14. (a) 18
  (b) (i) 3   **(ii)** 2.5
    (iii) 2.39
  (c) 3

15. (b) (i) 2 days   **(ii)** 2 days
    (iii) 2.4 days
  (c) 40%

16. (a) $740   **(b)** $650
  (c) $900

17. (a) 3   **(b)** 30
  (c) 3.87 books

18. (a) $z = 10$ **(b)** $11\frac{1}{5}$

19. (a) $(w - 15)$, $(w - 9)$, $(w - 3)$, $(w + 5)$, $(w + 6)$, $(w + 10)$
  (b) (i) $w + 1$ **(ii)** 19
  (c) 18

20. (a) 8
  (b) (i) 2.5 movies   **(ii)** 2.5 movies

Challenging Practice

21. (c) (i) Mean for $A = 251\frac{1}{6}$ g
           Means for $B = 251\frac{1}{12}$ g
    (ii) MAD for $A = 1\frac{13}{36}$ g
           MAD for $B = 1\frac{17}{18}$ g
  (d) Brand A: 8, Brand B: 7
  (e) Brand A

22. (a) (i) 13   **(ii)** 12 min
  (b) No
  (c) Jerome: $2\frac{2}{3}$ min, Shernise: $4\frac{1}{3}$ min
  (d) Jerome

23. (a) 11
  (b) 6
  (c) 3
  (d) Maximum value of $x = 25$
     Minimum value of $x = 9$

24. (a) $4x - 27$
  (b) 4
  (c) 15
  (d) (i) 14   **(ii)** 20

25. (a) $m = 10$
  (c) 40

Enrichment

26. (b) Questions 3 and 4

27. (a) 3   **(c)** 38 years old

28. 6

29. (a) Mean = 7, Median = 8, Modal score = 8

Chapter 16   Probability Of Simple Events

Basic Practice

1. (a) $A = \{1, 2, 3, 4, 5, 6\}$
  (b) $B = \{$Head, Tail$\}$
  (c) $C = \{\$0.01, \$0.05, \$0.10, \$0.25, \$0.50, \$1.00\}$
  (d) $E = \{$Earth, Venus, Saturn, Jupiter, Neptune, Mercury, Mars, Uranus$\}$
  (e) $F = \{$Belize, Costa Rica, El Salvador, Guatemala, Honduras, Nicaragua, Panama$\}$

2. **(a)** $U = \{1, 2, 4, 5, 10, 20\}$
   (b) $V = \{1, 2, 3, 6\}$
   (c) $W = \{4, 8, 12, 16, 20, 24, 28\}$
   (d) $X = \{15, 30, 45, 60\}$
   (e) $Y = \{1, 2, 3\}$
   (f) $Z = \{2, 3, 5, 7, 11, 13, 17, 19, 23, 29, 31, 37, 41, 43, 47\}$

3. **(a)** $A' = \{1, 8, 14\}$
   (b) $A' = \{d, m, p\}$
   (c) $A' = \{\text{red, orange, purple}\}$
   (d) $A' = \{1, 4, 6, 8, 9, 10\}$
   (e) $A' = \{2, 6, 10, 14, \ldots\}$
   (f) $A' = \{\quad\}$

4. **(a)** $\xi = \{a, e, g, i, n, o, p, r, s\}$,
      $S = \{g, i, n, p, r, s\}$
   (b) $S' = \{a, e, o\}$
   (c) $n(\xi) = 9, n(S) = 6, n(S') = 3$

5. **(a)** **(i)** $A' = \{\text{banking, transport}\}$
      (ii) $B' = \{\text{manufacturing, construction}\}$
   (b) B' is a subset of A.

6. **(a)** **(i)** $P \ne Q$
      (ii) $n(P) = n(Q)$
   (b) **(i)** $P' = \{6, 7, 11, 16\}$
      (ii) $Q' = \{6, 7, 8, 11\}$

7. **(a)** $\dfrac{3}{5}$　　**(b)** $\dfrac{2}{5}$　　**(c)** 0

8. **(a)** $\dfrac{1}{5}$　　**(b)** $\dfrac{4}{5}$　　**(c)** 1

9. **(a)** $\dfrac{1}{9}$　　**(b)** $\dfrac{4}{9}$　　**(c)** $\dfrac{4}{9}$

10. **(a)** $\dfrac{9}{16}$　　**(b)** $\dfrac{3}{16}$　　**(c)** $\dfrac{5}{8}$

11. **(a)** **(i)** $\dfrac{1}{4}$　　**(ii)** $\dfrac{3}{4}$
    (b) **(i)** $\dfrac{1}{8}$　　**(ii)** $\dfrac{7}{8}$

12. **(a)** Sample space, $S = \{2, 3, 5, 7, 11, 13, 17, 19, 23, 29\}$
    (b) **(i)** $W = \{11, 13, 17, 19, 23, 29\}$
       (ii) $P(W) = \dfrac{3}{5}, P(W') = \dfrac{2}{5}$

13. **(a)** Sample space, $S = \{AIM, AMI, IAM, IMA, MIA, MAI\}$
    (b) **(i)** $Q = \{AIM, IAM, MIA, MAI\}$
          $Q' = \{AMI, IMA\}$
       (ii) $P(Q) = \dfrac{2}{3}, P(Q') = \dfrac{1}{3}$

14. **(a)** $\dfrac{1}{2}$　　**(b)** $\dfrac{3}{8}$
    (c) $\dfrac{1}{2}$　　**(d)** $\dfrac{3}{4}$

15. **(a)** $\dfrac{8}{15}$　　**(b)** $\dfrac{1}{3}$
    (c) $\dfrac{1}{5}$　　**(d)** $\dfrac{2}{3}$

16. **(a)** $\dfrac{1}{4}$　　**(b)** $\dfrac{1}{8}$　　**(c)** $\dfrac{5}{8}$

Further Practice

17. **(a)** $\xi = \{\text{land vehicles}\}$
    (b) $\xi = \{\text{computer peripherals}\}$
    (c) $\xi = \{\text{kitchen utensils}\}$
    (d) $\xi = \{\text{military personnels}\}$
    (e) $\xi = \{\text{acute angles}\}$
    (f) $\xi = \{\text{real numbers}\}$

18. **(a)** **(i)** $P = \{a, e, i, m, s, t\}$
          $Q = \{a, c, e, h, i, m, s, t\}$
          $R = \{c, e, i, l, m, o, s, t, u\}$
       (ii) $n(P) = 6, n(Q) = 8, n(R) = 9$
    (b) **(i)** False
       (ii) True
       (iii) True
    (c) **(i)** $S = \{e, i, m, t\}, S \subset P$
       (ii) $S \subset Q$
       (iii) $P \subset Q$

19. **(a)** $A = \{1, 2, 3, 4, 5, 6, 7\}$,
       $B = \{6, 7, 8, 9, 10, 11, 12\}$
    (b) $A' = \{8, 9, 10, 11, 12\}$,
       $B' = \{1, 2, 3, 4, 5\}$

20. **(a)** $S = \{18, 27, 36, 45, 54, 63, 72, 81, 90\}$
       $T = \{9, 18, 27, 36, 45, 54, 63, 72, 81, 90, 99\}$
    (b) **(i)** $S \subset T$
       (ii) $T' \subset S'$
    (c) $n(S') = 90$
       $n(T') = 88$

21. **(a)** 15
    (b) 3 years
    (c) **(i)** $\dfrac{3}{16}$　　**(ii)** $\dfrac{3}{8}$　　**(iii)** $\dfrac{7}{16}$

22. **(a)** $1,343,639$
    (b) **(i)** $\dfrac{3}{7}$　　**(ii)** $\dfrac{2}{7}$　　**(iii)** 1

23. **(a)** $\dfrac{x}{60} = \dfrac{1}{4}$
    (b) $x + y = 32$
    (c) **(i)** $y = 17$　　**(ii)** $\dfrac{17}{60}$

24. **(a)** **(i)** Sample space, S
          $= \{1, 5, 7, 11, 13, 17, 19, 23, 25, 29, 31, 35, 37, 41, 43\}$
       (ii) 15
    (b) **(i)** $\dfrac{4}{5}$　　**(ii)** $\dfrac{1}{5}$　　**(iii)** $\dfrac{2}{5}$

25. (a) Sample space, S
= {MVJRS, MVRJS, MRVJS, MRJVS, MJRVS,
MJVRS, SVJRM, SVRJM, SRVJM, SRJVM,
SJRVM, SJVRM}

(b) $\frac{1}{3}$

(c) $P(A) = \frac{2}{3}$, $P(A') = \frac{1}{3}$

26. (a) Sample space, S
= {PQ, PR, PS, PT, PU, QR, QS, QT, QU, RS, RT, RU,
ST, SU, TU}

(b) (i) $\frac{1}{3}$ **(ii)** $\frac{1}{15}$

(iii) $\frac{4}{15}$

27. (a) Sample space, S
= {(–9, 2), (–9, –3), (–9, 9), (3, 2), (3, –3), (3, 9), (1, 2),
(1, –3), (1, 9)}

(b) (i) $\frac{5}{9}$ **(ii)** $\frac{5}{9}$

28. (a) Sample space, S
= {(T, H, H), (H, H, T), (H, T, H), (T, T, H),
(T, H, T), (H, T, T), (T, T, T), (H, H, H)}

(b) (i) $\frac{1}{8}$ **(ii)** $\frac{3}{8}$

(iii) $\frac{1}{2}$ **(iv)** $\frac{1}{8}$

29. (a) $\frac{9}{64}$ **(b)** $\frac{5}{8}$ **(c)** $\frac{15}{64}$

Challenging Practice

30. (b) (i) $Q \subset P$ **(ii)** $P' \subset Q'$

31. (a) $x = 2$ **(b)** 30

(c) $\frac{1}{10}$ **(d)** $\frac{7}{12}$

32. (a) 88 blue buttons, 112 green buttons
(b) 18
(c) 16
(d) 12

33. (a) Sample space, S
= {(G, B), (G, W), (G, G), (R, B), (R, W), (R, G),
(B, B), (B, W), (B, G), (Y, B), (Y, W), (Y, G)}

(b) (i) $\frac{1}{4}$ **(ii)** $\frac{1}{3}$

(c) $P(M) = \frac{1}{6}$, $P(M') = \frac{5}{6}$

34. (a) Sample space, S
= {ABC, ABD, ABE, ACD, ACE, ADE, BCD, BCE,
BDE, CDE}

(b) $P(X) = \frac{3}{5}$, $P(X') = \frac{2}{5}$

(c) (i) Y = {ACD, BDE, ACE, ABD, BCE}

(ii) $\frac{1}{2}$

Enrichment

35. (a) (i) ϕ, {apple}

(ii) ϕ, {banana}, {mango}, {banana, mango}

(iii) ϕ, {cherry}, {mango}, {pear}, {cherry, mango},
{cherry, pear}, {mango, pear},
{cherry, mango, pear}

(b) 2^n

(c) ξ is the set of all fruits.

36. (a) $\frac{1}{10}$ **(b)** $\frac{1}{100}$ **(c)** 1

37. (b) $\frac{7}{10}$

(c) (i) $\frac{1}{4}$ **(ii)** $\frac{1}{10}$

38. (a) $A - B - C - G, A - B - F - G, A - E - F - G$

(b) $\frac{2}{3}$

39. (a) 1,500

Chapter 17   Probability Of Combined Events

Basic Practice

1. (a) $\frac{1}{3}$ **(b)** $\frac{2}{3}$

(c) $\frac{1}{2}$ **(d)** 0

2. (a) $S = \{1, 2, 3, 4, 5, 6\}$

(b) (i) $\frac{1}{2}$ **(ii)** $\frac{1}{2}$ **(iii)** $\frac{5}{6}$

(iv) $\frac{1}{6}$ **(v)** $\frac{1}{3}$

3. (a) $\frac{2}{5}$ **(b)** $\frac{6}{25}$

(c) $\frac{1}{5}$ **(d)** $\frac{2}{25}$

(e) $\frac{3}{25}$

4. (b) (i) $\frac{1}{8}$ **(ii)** $\frac{1}{4}$ **(iii)** $\frac{3}{4}$

5. (b) (i) $\frac{1}{6}$ **(ii)** $\frac{5}{12}$

(iii) $\frac{7}{12}$ **(iv)** $\frac{1}{12}$

6. (b) (i) $\frac{1}{9}$ **(ii)** $\frac{2}{9}$ **(iii)** $\frac{1}{3}$

(iv) $\frac{2}{3}$ **(v)** $\frac{4}{9}$

7. (b) (i) $\frac{1}{25}$ **(ii)** $\frac{16}{25}$ **(iii)** $\frac{4}{25}$

(iv) $\frac{8}{25}$ **(v)** $\frac{9}{25}$ **(vi)** $\frac{24}{25}$

8. (b) (i) $\dfrac{7}{15}$ (ii) $\dfrac{8}{15}$

      (iii) $\dfrac{2}{5}$ (iv) $\dfrac{3}{5}$

9. (a) $\dfrac{1}{40}$ **(b)** $\dfrac{3}{10}$

   (c) $\dfrac{9}{40}$

10. (a) $\dfrac{121}{400}$ **(b)** $\dfrac{3}{8}$

   (c) $\dfrac{3}{16}$ **(d)** $\dfrac{1}{4}$

   (e) $\dfrac{27}{80}$

Further Practice

11. (a) $\dfrac{1}{2,197}$ **(b)** $\dfrac{8}{27}$

   (c) $\dfrac{1}{27}$ **(d)** $\dfrac{1}{3}$

   (e) $\dfrac{6}{2,197}$

12. (a) $\dfrac{1}{32}$ **(b)** $\dfrac{3}{32}$

   (c) $\dfrac{1}{32}$ **(d)** $\dfrac{7}{32}$

13. (a) $\dfrac{1}{26}$ **(b)** $\dfrac{9}{13}$

   (c) $\dfrac{1}{13}$ **(d)** $\dfrac{5}{26}$

   (e) $\dfrac{21}{26}$

14. (a) (i) $\dfrac{5}{12}$ (ii) $\dfrac{2}{3}$

      (iii) $\dfrac{1}{3}$

   (b) (ii) (a) $\dfrac{9}{55}$ (b) $\dfrac{1}{220}$

          (c) $\dfrac{21}{55}$ (d) $\dfrac{34}{55}$

15. (a) $x = 50$

   (b) Sector D. Angle of sector D is the smallest.

   (c) (i) $\dfrac{205}{648}$ (ii) $\dfrac{443}{648}$

   (d) $\dfrac{23}{144}$

16. (b) (i) $\dfrac{2}{5}$ (ii) $\dfrac{4}{15}$

      (iii) $\dfrac{1}{6}$

17. (a) Yes. 1,000 units are available separately for investors who subscribe for 1, 5, and 10 units.

   (b) (i) $\dfrac{1}{180}$ (ii) $\dfrac{73}{180}$

      (iii) $\dfrac{47}{180}$

18. (a) $\dfrac{4,913}{8,000}$ **(b)** $\dfrac{44}{125}$

   (c) $\dfrac{2,299}{4,000}$

Challenging Practice

19. (a) $\dfrac{3}{4}$ **(b)** $\dfrac{3}{256}$

   (c) $\dfrac{1}{256}$

20. (b) $\dfrac{1}{10}$

   (c) (i) $\dfrac{209}{250}$ (ii) $\dfrac{41}{250}$

21. (a) $\dfrac{7}{20}$

   (b) The game is not fair since the probability of winning is less than $\dfrac{1}{2}$.

22. $\dfrac{1}{4}$

23. 0.42525

Enrichment

24. (a) $\dfrac{1}{1,024}$ **(b)** $\dfrac{781}{1,024}$

   (c) $\dfrac{405}{1,024}$ **(d)** 1

25. (a) $k = 0.4 \left(\text{or } \dfrac{2}{5}\right)$

   (b) (i) 0.251   (ii) 0.6156

26. (a) (i) $\dfrac{5}{9}$ (ii) $\dfrac{1}{3}$

      (iii) $\dfrac{1}{9}$

   (b) (i) The possible scores are 2, 4, 6, 8, and 10.

      (ii) $P(\text{score} = 2) = \dfrac{25}{81}$

          $P(\text{score} = 4) = \dfrac{10}{27}$

          $P(\text{score} = 6) = \dfrac{19}{81}$

          $P(\text{score} = 8) = \dfrac{2}{27}$

          $P(\text{score} = 10) = \dfrac{1}{81}$

27. (a) 0.999975

   (b) 0.999925

The **Dimensions Math Workbooks** are written as supplements to the textbooks in the Dimensions Math series for middle school students. They are designed to give the students more practice in applying the concepts learned.

The questions in each workbook chapter are categorized into 4 parts according to the level of difficulty and the thinking skills involved.

These comprehensive workbooks aim to give students the tools and the confidence to handle mathematical questions and apply mathematical concepts to real-life situations. By achieving this, students will find that learning mathematics is an interesting and exciting experience.

ISBN 978-981-4431-75-0

9 789814 431750